THE FACE OF RURAL AMERICA

THE FACE OF RURAL AMERICA

 THE 1976 YEARBOOK OF AGRICULTURE
IS A VISUAL RECORD OF AMERICA'S AGRICULTURE
IN THE BICENTENNIAL YEAR.
PUBLISHED BY THE UNITED STATES
DEPARTMENT OF AGRICULTURE

For sale by the Superintendent of Documents,
U.S. Government Printing Office
Washington, D.C. 20402 - Price $7.30

Stock No. 001—000—03521—5
Catalog No. A 1.10:976
LCC 76—3089

CONTENTS

INTRODUCTION

If someone had been able to put together a good book of photographs in 1776 showing Colonial life as it really was, that book would be invaluable today. It would bring early America to life for us in a way words alone cannot do.

As we thought about this, we decided that we wouldn't miss the opportunity to photograph America's farm life for the 1976 Bicentennial.

This book captures, photographically, American rural life as it is today. Not only will the book become more valuable with each passing year, but its first purpose is to help you understand better right now what modern farming is really like.

Modern agriculture is changing so fast that it is hard to keep up. Those who "used to live on a farm" may have fond memories of those experiences, but if they are away from the farm for even a while, they quickly fall behind.

It is nothing short of amazing to see the new machines in agriculture, and the new techniques. Farms are getting larger, as they should. A farmer with a couple of tractors, self-propelled harvesters, finishing houses for livestock, and a feed mixer with automated feeding equipment can do a great deal more than a farmer could with horses, a scoop shovel, and hand harvesting. He can easily handle more acres—and he needs to in order to pay for the equipment and meet his increased operating expenses.

These are still family farms, as much as they were with "40 acres and a mule." The family is still providing the labor and the management. It's just that the family can do so much more.

A few benchmarks give a glimpse of the progress: Over the last 20 years, the output per hour on the farm has increased more than three times as fast as output per man hour in non-farm activities. Whereas one farm worker produced enough to feed himself and 19 others 20 years ago, he can now feed 56 besides himself.

Corn yields per acre have more than doubled over the last 20 years; wheat yields are up 55 percent. Soybean production is three times as much as it was 20 years ago. In the same time, beef consumption per person is up 46 percent; poultry, up 85 percent.

We have become so efficient that we are way and above the world's largest exporter of farm products—nearly $22 billion in 1975. That's 3½ times as much as 10 years earlier. Since we imported about $10 billion of farm products in 1975, we had a favorable balance of $12 billion in agricultural trade. This made jobs for hundreds of thousands of Americans, and enabled us to buy imported automobiles, much-needed petroleum, and a wide array of consumer goods that mean so much to the level of living of American consumers.

The photographs in the book have captured some of the flavor of this pulsating, efficient, productive agriculture—and the qualities of the farm people.

This is the current Yearbook of Agriculture. We've been publishing Yearbooks since 1894. Usually they are mainly text on a useful subject for both urban and rural people. Some of the earlier books are now collector's items; and some of the picture pages from earlier Yearbooks are sold separately at antique shows.

For this 1976 Yearbook we assembled a group of nearly 60 photographers—some private photographers, some from Land-Grant Universities, and some from the Department of Agriculture. We asked them to use their cameras throughout 1975 to photograph typical rural America at work and at play.

The photographers, in carrying out their assignments, covered the nation looking for good photographs. They did not follow a preconceived plan to record every aspect of farming, or all commodities, or all breeds of livestock, or all machinery, or all activity in all parts of the nation. Rather, this is a broad collection of representative photographs of what goes on in rural America as seen through the camera of photographers who were there when it happened.

You will discover, as you look at this panorama of modern farming, that today's agriculture, while still essentially a family business, is predominantly big and commercial—and human.

The family lives and works on the farm, with each member sharing in the successes and disappointments. The entire family pitches in, from the young children to the grandparents. The wife is a strong partner with her husband in the farming operation, sharing the work and planning. There's a high risk from the weather, insects, and diseases; and bitter disappointments as prices fall just when the farmer is ready to market his year's crop or his livestock. But there are other times of outstanding success and great satisfaction. This makes for strong, independent, resourceful people with a deep faith and optimism, and a robust ability to enjoy life along with the work.

You'll like the book, we're sure, and 100 years from now, or 200, succeeding generations will be eternally grateful that *The Face of Rural America* captured what rural life was really like "back in the old days of 1976."

Earl L. Butz
Secretary of Agriculture

LAND

Overleaf   PHOTOGRAPHED BY WILSON
Farmers in their quest for land to raise
food for the nation have tamed the steep
hillsides of the Palouse in eastern
Washington, turning it into a virtual
garden of waving grain, producing 50 or
more bushels of wheat to the acre. That's
the equivalent of 3,500 loaves of bread
for each acre.

E verything springs from the land—most importantly the
   food that sustains man's life. The land is a fragile
productive mantle of topsoil that Nature has laid atop
stone, clay and sand. There, the roots of crops that man
has developed stand in a few inches of topsoil, feeding
on nutrients dissolved by rainfall, while their leafy tops
capture the sun's rays to manufacture sugars, starches, fats
and proteins. Farmers, through centuries, have developed
the art of tilling and care that has increased food
production enough to support today's population. Can
they increase production fast enough to feed the
population of future years?

O'REAR

Where volcanoes threw up molten lava
tens of millions of years ago to form the
Hawaiian Islands, man now grows
sugarcane and pineapples amidst
subtropical greenery and a thriving tourist
business. Above are acres of sugarcane
grown near Pearl Harbor on Oahu. Of the
112,000 acres devoted to principal crop
production in the Hawaiian Islands in
1975, about 105,600 acres were devoted
to the production of sugarcane.

WRIGHT

Ranching often is a rugged, lonely way of
life. At times, with cattle prices depressed,
the main compensation it seems, is the
natural beauty of the setting, such as this
one near Daniel, Wyoming.

Opposite page
Rangeland around Guymon, Oklahoma,
was called "No Man's Land" when the
Hitch family settled in 1884. In the 1930's
it was the dustbowl, but today, thanks to
improved farming methods and irrigation,
that land is fertile and flourishing.
Cattle drink at a stock tank filled with
water by "wind power."

In contrast with the scattered ranches and wide open spaces of the West, the land near Roaring Spring in south central Pennsylvania has been turned into family dairies, orchards and fields of hay and corn. Farmers have kept it as fertile as it was 200 years ago.

Working the land, Harold Crawford, a small Missouri farmer, prepares a 10-acre piece for corn. Average farm size in the U.S. is around 385 acres.

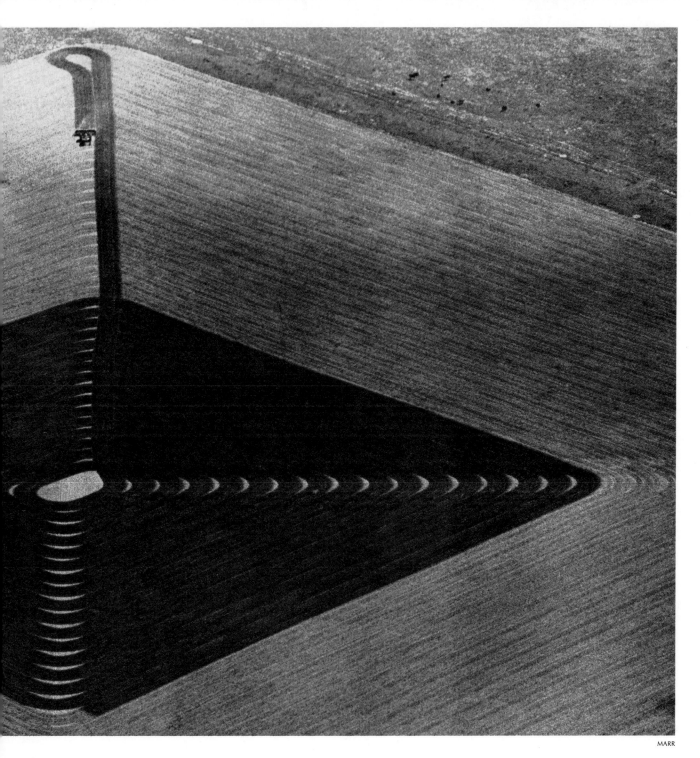

A heavy tractor molds patterns in the land
as a huge field in the Oklahoma panhandle
is planted to milo. Tremendous
investments in machinery, fertilizer, land
and labor are needed before a crop ever
goes into the ground. Farming is a living
"hope" that there will be a paying harvest.

Diverse patterns of the land are more
clearly defined from the air or from afar.
Near Wahiawa, Oahu, Hawaii, plastic strips
protect a newly-planted pineapple field,
and form a ribbon-like motif.

Top of page
The All American Canal is the umbilical
cord for the Imperial and Coachella Valleys
in southern California, carrying water from
the Colorado River through the desolate
Sand Hills for farm irrigation. Throughout
the U.S., more than 27 million acres of
crops, 8 million acres of hay, and $4\frac{1}{2}$
million acres of pasture are irrigated at
considerable expense.

PICKERELL

Above

American farmers grow half the corn produced in the world, and devote more land to corn than to any other crop. This field, near Kearney, Nebraska, will yield a bumper crop—perhaps 150 bushels per acre. The average U.S. yield in 1975: 86.2 bushels per acre.

Circular shapes formed on the Washington landscape result from mammoth circular irrigation systems.

OTIS

O'REAR

Dairy farms are nestled in the Matanuska
Valley below Pioneer Mountain, near
Palmer, Alaska. There are serious
limitations, as well as strong potentials,
for agricultural development in our largest
state. Plant scientists are breeding new
vegetables, legumes and grasses that will
adapt to Alaska's soil and climate.

The United States has 2.3 billion acres of land, more than half of it used to produce crops and livestock. Our nation has a large acreage of potential cropland that is presently used for pasture and forest because of high costs of bringing it into crop production and operating it. Mountain regions do provide rangeland and grazing for livestock, primarily cattle and sheep. Thus, land that otherwise would be unproductive is a source of beef and lamb for our dinner tables.

With the Sierra Nevada as a backdrop, a flock of 1,000 sheep harvests sparse grass near Bridgeport, California.

A seldom-used barn and corral await cows
and cowboys as sunrise uncovers the
Tetons in western Wyoming. Cattle
roundups are still held on many ranches
in the West.

Next page — PHOTOGRAPHED BY WRIGHT

Hereford cows and calves head for fresh pastures on the ranch operated by the Norman Pape family, near Daniel, Wyoming.

A team of horses hauls hay to cattle on the Myron Loomis ranch, outside Donnelly, Idaho. Not every chore is mechanized on farms, and a few farmers and ranchers keep work horses for odd jobs. Because of the popularity of riding horses, horse population is at an all-time high in the U.S., an estimated 8½ million head.

DEVORE

The South can claim some of America's oldest farmland. George Washington, for example, was one of those Virginia planters who raised tobacco and exported it to England more than 200 years ago. Tobacco is still raised today in Virginia, but it is no longer strictly a southern crop; tobacco is grown in 25 states.

Moss-draped cypress trees frame the field as tobacco is transplanted on the Charles Johnson farm, near Conway, South Carolina.

24

ALEXANDER

Cutting and staking of burley tobacco, part
of the harvesting process, takes place
under a September sky and canopy of
clouds near Vevay, Indiana, on the John
B. Stevens farm, just across the Ohio
River from Kentucky. Tobacco is a crop
that has defied mechanization, and much
costly hand work is still required.
However, machines that efficiently
harvest tobacco are being developed,
and are expected to see widespread
use in a few years.

A Basque shepherd with his grazing flock in a tranquil forest meadowland is a familiar sight in Arizona.

On farms, trees are grown generally on land that is uneconomical for other crops. Farmer forestry includes the marketing of lumber, posts and greenery; Christmas tree growing; a family wood lot; and maple syrup production. A third of the Nation's total land area, including Alaska—754 million acres—is in forests. Nearly 200 million acres of woodland is grazed. While very little of the forested acreage in Alaska is harvested for wood products, almost 80 percent of the forest land in the 48 contiguous states is commercially productive. But the forests provide more than wood and grazing opportunities. They offer, among still other benefits, recreation to millions of urban Americans.

Opposite page
Fred Williams takes a bore sample to determine a tree's age in this pine forest in Shannon County, Missouri. About 45 percent of the Nation's timber harvest comes from the South, and the South is expected to be the major timber producer in the future.

E very year, a quarter million acres of cropland are gobbled up by urban development, right-of-ways, highways, and airports. This urban encroachment drives up the cost of farmland, increases the taxes on farms bordering suburbia, and reduces the amount of productive farm land.

Alternate strips of crops help save soil and water. Farmers are the original conservationists who, in order to maintain a paying farm, need to keep the soil and water in place. Soil and water are the main foundation of a successful crop. Soil can't be worked too wet or it will lose its tilth. Fertility must be maintained to support good yields. Nowadays, farmers are also maintaining wildlife habitats in their conservation plans.

When Spring's warmth engulfs the Corn Belt, which extends from Ohio through Iowa, farm machinery rolls over the land, planting 77 million acres to corn in a matter of days. With its rich soil, good climate, and sufficient rainfall, the Corn Belt is unexcelled for farming.

PEOPLE

Overleaf PHOTOGRAPHED BY MARR

With the do-it-yourself attitude commonplace among farmers everywhere, Leroy "Tilly" Tillotson attaches a sideboard extension to the top of his truck, enabling him to haul additional bushels of wheat to the grain elevator 18 miles away in Farnam, Nebraska.

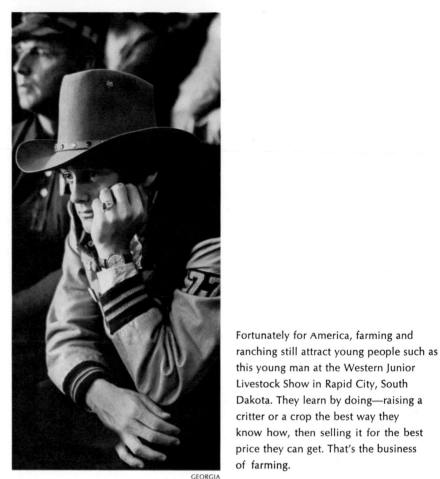

GEORGIA

Fortunately for America, farming and ranching still attract young people such as this young man at the Western Junior Livestock Show in Rapid City, South Dakota. They learn by doing—raising a critter or a crop the best way they know how, then selling it for the best price they can get. That's the business of farming.

The great strength of America's agriculture is her people. They comprise less than five percent of our population. The average farm worker (owner, family help and hired help) produces enough to feed and clothe himself and 56 other persons—an increase of 3½ times the 15 people in 1950. This potent productivity is unmatched anywhere in today's world, and unmatched in history. The people on our land represent many nationalities, and enterprises: there are corn and hog farmers, cattlemen, poultry raisers, citrus growers, organic farmers, and dozens of other kinds. Although every farm or ranch is unique and differs from its neighbors, rural Americans possess many similar characteristics. One is willingness to share their best farming ideas with other farmers. Most farmers are regarded as conservative minded, yet the nature of their business compels them to take high risks . . . they are gamblers, in a sense, though most rebel at being called such. Conservative on the one hand, farmers nevertheless are innovative and adaptive to new farming techniques. They seem to thrive on hard work, and have a profound love—a reverence—for the land they till.

Opposite page
The J. Brewer Bottorffs, lifelong farmers, have been married more than 50 years. Family portraits hang in the living room of their farm home near St. James, Missouri. Farming is a family business, with man, wife, and children sharing the daily work, the income, the joys, the successes and disappointments.

34

BAER

Nearly everyone—of every age—is
caught up in excitement of activities at
the Ohio State Fair in Columbus.

MCDOUGALL

Statistics show that the average age of today's farmer is about 50. Recently young people have begun to return to the farm, and enrollments in agricultural colleges have climbed dramatically (22.5 percent from 1972 to 1974) as farm-reared and non-farm youth are attracted to farming's future and the task of feeding the world. Agriculture offers new opportunities and attractions for young people that didn't exist even five years ago, and though it isn't easy to get started in farming, it never has been.

A willingness to share an idea that works, and an eagerness to learn, are farm traits that boost food output. This group soaks up facts and figures about a new hog production setup, during a young farmers' tour in the Midwest.

Opposite page
Mr. and Mrs. Luis Avila grow fruit and
vegetables and sell them at this roadside
stand in Chimayo, New Mexico, thus
eliminating the "middleman's" margin.
Farmers get only about 40¢ of the
consumer's food dollar.

After a day of working in the lettuce fields,
Mexican farm workers are bused back to
the Mexican border at Calexico, California.
Fewer farm hands and migrant workers are
needed as agriculture becomes more
mechanized. There are an estimated
209,000 migratory farm workers in the U.S.

Some farmers, such as John Elmore, are large operators. He has a radio-equipped car so he can keep in touch with his foremen in the Imperial Valley of southern California. Nationwide, nine of every 10 farms are family-sized units using family labor and occasional hired help.

Higher production costs and a roller
coaster, up-and-down hog market are
concerns of Dan Kostelak (left) and
his brother, Frank. While prices of farm
products fluctuate, most other prices—
including the ones farmers pay—go
up and stay up.

As flames swept through their dairy barn completely destroying the building, milking equipment, and feed, Ronald and Jane Nipple were faced with a tough decision. Their fire insurance wasn't adequate to cover the loss. Should they give up farm life and sell out? Neighbors encouraged them to stay on, offering more than words— they offered to rebuild the barn. On several consecutive Saturdays, a dozen or more neighborhood men showed up with hammers, nails, saws, and levels, and the new 40 x 140-foot barn began to take shape . . . built from oak lumber grown on the Nipples' own farm. The women served a hearty, noon-time meal on the lawn, and carted hot coffee to the building site. There was fun and fellowship—and a barn got built. The Nipples expressed their sentiments in a thank-you note that concluded, "We have prospered in knowing and having such wonderful rural neighbors. God bless them." Such acts have built rural America.

PHOTOGRAPHED BY WITTE

Top of page
The auctioneer's banter at a Mississippi sales barn amuses the crowd. But the farmer who sells his cattle sees a whole year's work sold in two minutes—for what a buyer will pay that particular day.

Everyone should take time now and then just to relax and be together, especially if it's a fall day in Virginia. Ann Heizer and her daughter Carol, 8, who live on a dairy farm, know that kings, potentates and millionaires can't buy anything that will equal the splendor of October colors on the Virginia hills.

Opposite page
Jeff Stringer, of Hutchinson, Kansas, has helped his uncle, Ralph Hansen, of Kingfisher, Oklahoma, with the wheat harvest the past several summers. Some are bumper harvests, some don't do much more than get the seed back. It's like life. "It all evens out," Hansen explained philosophically to his nephew.

ALEXANDER

MARR

LUSTIG

SCHUMAKER

O'REAR

MARR

WARREN

ROBINSON

O'REAR

WARREN

BAER

BOGRE

SUTTON

ALEXANDER

CARNAHAN

S ome of the varied faces of American agriculture . . . a migrant worker, a rancher, an organic farmer, a wheat grower, a livestockman, a part-time farmer . . . all, and others, are shown here, and each has a role in America's agricultural abundance.

Left to right, top to bottom: Ken Johnston, Ohio; Jim Lancaster, Oklahoma; Hilda Newland, Maryland; Fred Shaw, Mississippi; Sam Shuey, Ohio; Charles Shutes, Arkansas; Brenda Wright, Vermont; Victor Sease, California; Chuck Grimes, Oklahoma; Inger Sessions, New Jersey; Leslie May, Indiana; John Reese, Ohio; Lovenia Patrick, Mississippi; Ben Wilcox, Maine; Stan Otani, Hawaii; Dick Roberts, Alaska.

O'REAR

47

Gerry Schultheis, 18, and his grandfather,
Jacob F. Schultheis, 77, rest while a
combine is repaired in eastern Washington.
The art and fine points of farming are
passed from generation to generation.

Even in Biblical times, the question of keeping the farm
in the family was a prime concern. Who will get the
farm when the parents die? What with the hard work and
all, who will *want* the farm when that time comes?
Which child will borrow to buy out the interests of the
other survivors? There are other questions: Will
inheritance taxes make it possible to keep the same
name on the barn another generation? What about
incorporation? And, after all, is the farm large enough
to continue to compete successfully? There's a lot to
talk over. Grandfather wants to pass on wisdom, a
hard-earned commodity that's never obsolete. A risk of
the father—a big investment in land or machinery, for
instance—affects the future of his children. Should the
risk be taken? They need to talk it out together.

Ken Walker of Faribault, Minnesota, left,
was active in 4-H and the Future Farmers
of America in high school but then he
tried truck driving. In a couple of years, he
was back to take over the farm his father,
Dan, has been working for 25 years.

Barbara and Greg Nelson live in a mobile
home on a farm near Delavan, Illinois.
Greg, like many young people entering
farming, has a college degree.

Louise Swanson grew up on a tractor seat and can handle a 4-bottom plow with ease in the loamy soil of southern Minnesota. A senior at the University of Minnesota, St. Paul, she is studying home economics. Her campus life is typical of students in her curriculum with one notable exception. During the Spring planting and Fall harvesting seasons, Louise goes home at least once and often twice a week, to help with field work on the family farm. Her father, Walter Swanson, farms 800 acres of corn, rye, and oats, and raises hogs and Shorthorn cattle near Hastings, Minnesota. He has four daughters and one son, plus two foster children. During the busy seasons, everyone pitches in to get field work completed as quickly as possible, and this is when Louise trades her classroom chair for a tractor seat.

PHOTOGRAPHED BY BRENEMAN

51

O'REAR

In 1968, about 200 Russian immigrants established a village called Nikolaevsk on the Kenai Peninsula, Alaska. They wear colorful clothing and call themselves "Old Believers." They became U.S. citizens last year.

Opposite page
Earl Booms, 43, is a dairy and grain farmer in Huron County, Michigan. He owns 250 acres, rents 300, and milks 60 cows. Fifteen years ago, 60-cow dairy herds were few and far between. Today they are common as herds continue to increase in size.

Racing through a cornfield like a halfback running for the end zone, young Tracy Shutes, of near El Dorado, Arkansas, exemplifies the thoughts of most Americans: the farm is a great place to live. For the first time in decades, the migration from the land into our nation's cities has ceased. In fact, the trend has suddenly and dramatically reversed itself. Today, more and more people are moving to the suburbs, small towns, rural communities, and "back to the land."

MACHINES

Overleaf   PHOTOGRAPHED BY BOGRE

A powerful 8-wheeled tractor can cost
as much as $50,000—a few cost more.
The cab has air-conditioning, an AM-FM
radio, and a special seat, important
comforts for young farmer Ronnie Lyons,
who often spends 12 hours a day driving
the tractor.

BJORK

Like a pilot in a cockpit, Pennsylvania
dairyman Ron Mowry controls the tractor
and the rig it pulls. The rig chops and
shreds whole stalks of ripe corn, making
a feed that cows relish.

F amily farms are larger today because a man with
modern equipment can handle a lot more acres than
a man with a hoe or a man with a span of mules and
a walking plow. Mechanical power has replaced muscle
power. A decade ago only five percent of the farm
tractors sold were rated at 90 horsepower or more. Now
about half are that large. The value of machinery and
motor vehicles on the average farm is about $20,000.

Opposite page
Two combines, two trucks, and a giant
tractor ply the Palouse hillsides in
Washington. If the combines and tractor
had to be replaced new, it would cost
this wheat farmer a cool $150,000. He has
to raise a lot of wheat to make ends meet.

Today's food moves on rubber tires.
There must be around 70 million of them
on the nation's 2.8 million farms.
Harvested crops roll from field to storage
for feeding. Then . . .

. . . finished livestock roll to market.
The amount of rubber in the equipment
farmers buy every year would put tires
on 7 million automobiles.

RUNNING

60

Mechanization has drastically changed the face of farming. Just a generation ago, horse-drawn equipment was the rule, and farming was hard physical work. Hot, dusty, throbbing threshing machines that required a big crew have been replaced by combines with glassed-in cabs with many comforts for the operator. The substitution of machinery for labor helps explain why in recent years farm output per man-hour has increased more than three times as fast as output per man-hour in industry.

Modern machines extend a farmer's day, allowing him to spend additional hours in the field during the critical planting and harvesting seasons—often till long after sunset. No horses to get tired; only the farmer.

CONKLIN

WARREN

Farm machines do the darndest things. This "feed buggy" fires specially-formulated pellets into a pond on a catfish farm in the South.

You can smell the newly-turned ribbons of earth when a huge tractor and plow prepare an Indiana field for a new crop. A rig this size will plow 60 acres per day; a team of horses would turn about 2 acres.

Opposite Page
This unit will plant six rows of soybeans in one sweep for Marvin Robinson, Audrain County, Missouri. Big equipment is needed to get the crop in fast while the sun shines.

Farm tractors perform double-duty—and
then some. The same tractor may be used
to mow a hayfield, then rake it, and
later to pull the baler which will bale the
hay. The smaller, utility tractors handle
dozens of odd jobs around the farm. As
farms become larger, there's a trend
toward self-propelled, specialized
equipment.

Trucks help move livestock, from one section of the country to another, to better pastures, to feedlots, to livestock markets.

Farm machines are eminently and practically designed to accomplish special jobs. This machine is designed to work in cranberry bogs in Long Beach, Washington.

Agricultural equipment must frequently
travel the highways and rural roads. Many
farmers operate farms miles apart. The
familiar, triangular-shaped SMV (Slow
Moving Vehicle) signs on the rear of
tractors and equipment remind motorists
to slow down.

Today's commercial farms use machines of many sizes and descriptions. There are tillage tools, hay and forage harvesting equipment, planters and seeders, harvesters and combines. Certain industrial-type machines, such as the skid-steer loader (above), adapt themselves to the farm, whose owners now wonder "how did we ever get along without them?" This one solves a drainage problem in a barnyard on a New York dairy farm.

Farm boys take to machinery like a duck to water. Boys such as John Ray, of Mason County, West Virginia start with miniature farm equipment.

Top of page
Weird-looking machine with fat tires can go just about anywhere—that's why it's used on the farm. This one is used to check irrigated fields which are muddy and hard to reach otherwise.

Above
Sophisticated farm machine with a space-age appearance, this equipment digs trenches and lays tile or pipe to drain wet farmland. Laser beam principle aids digging process.

Overleaf
The farmer of 1976 has not entirely
replaced hand tools with machinery,
though many of the tools get less and
less use each year.

PHOTOGRAPHED BY O'REAR

O'REAR

Farm families have always been big on
growing gardens for home-grown food.
Mechanization helps there, too. As any
farmer knows, a motor-driven tiller is a
much faster, easier way to weed the
sweet corn than by hand.

On a smaller scale, power tools serve rural Americans
in the same manner as tractors and big pieces of
equipment—they save labor, save time, and put farm
chores on a business basis by increasing output
and efficiency.

ROBINSON

R. CLARK

He who cuts his own wood gets warmed twice. Well, hardly any more with a power saw, such as on this tree farm in Maine.

An Ohio farmer and orchard owner keeps his radio-telephone stashed away in a mailbox mounted on his tractor. Farmers need to keep in touch with the markets and suppliers.

The farmer has to be a jack of all trades. For one thing, he may not be able to afford to hire specialists—or wait for one to get to his farm. So he learns to do as much as he can by himself—or with the help of family and friends. Being "handy" saves money that otherwise would be lost from "down time."

As any mechanic will testify, sometimes you need four hands to fix something. That's when you call for help. In this case, Richard Conover and wife Patricia of Ulster, Pennsylvania are fixing a hay baler together on their dairy farm.

A sheared pin shuts down a haying
operation until repairs are made. Because
of mechanization, farmers as a group
incur many injuries. Farming can be
dangerous—it ranks third behind
construction and mining as the most
accident-prone occupation.

Even the most sophisticated looking
machines break down—out in the field
in the middle of a job, of course. Ira
D. McClurkin of Montgomery County,
Alabama acts as a "dentist" to a combine
in a soybean field.

SHERBELL

75

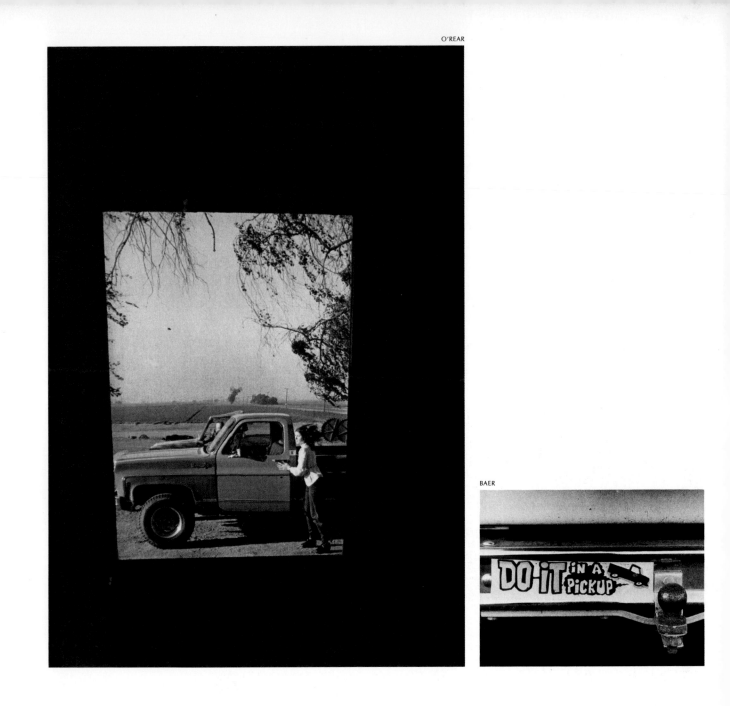

BAER

Pickup trucks perform a variety of duties for farm
families. They are used to run to town for spare parts;
check the range and cattle; and provide a front row seat for
the parade. They are a great help in building a fence;
are fine for catching a noonday snooze; and sometimes
come equipped with radio transmitters. Bumper stickers
are a personal touch.

RUNNING

BRENEMAN

MCDOUGALL

R. CLARK

BRENEMAN

ALLARD

F arm needs for equipment and supplies make farmers a big customer in the nation's economy. In fact, agriculture is the main customer for such basic industries as petroleum, chemicals, rubber and steel. Farm families can work more land with the newer machines—but it takes more land to produce enough to pay for the equipment. This need for extra land causes tremendous competition among neighbors when a farm comes up for sale, pushing land prices sky high. High land prices, in turn, force farmers to raise all the crops or livestock they can to pay for the land and machinery. They have to keep hopping to stay ahead. This pressure to keep efficient lowers the cost of producing each bushel or pound—a reason why U.S. consumers get more food at less cost than consumers anywhere else in the world.

Airplanes play an increasingly important role in modern day agriculture. Aerial crop spraying is essential for certain crops. Planes are used for seeding, too.

O'REAR

Trail bikes aren't playthings on the farm or ranch. Oklahoman Chuck Grimes uses his to check on his cows and bulls, or round them up.

Is this the farm machine prototype of the future . . . computer-like equipment as scientifically programmed as a satellite? Will tomorrow's machines be automatically propelled with pneumatic, mechanical, hydraulic, or electrical power—or by some energy source not yet known? Perhaps today's irrigation rigs that "walk" their fields where and when they're told are a preview of what's ahead for farm machines as America heads into her third century. This sprinkler irrigation rig revives the land near Abbott, New Mexico.

WEATHER

Overleaf　　　PHOTOGRAPHED BY WILSON
Dawn in a land blessed with favorable
weather brings a new promise of plenty.
The early morning light announces another
workday where farm people will harness
the forces of nature to make the earth
bloom and prosper.

MARR

Farmers and ranchers are at the weather's mercy. Still,
the United States, for the most part, is blessed with
moderate, favorable weather which enables this country to
grow enormous quantities of food, and to live up to its
title as "the breadbasket of the world."

Menacing clouds hang heavy over a
stretch of wheat land, threatening a
bumper crop. Farmers everywhere eye
each approaching storm with apprehension,
knowing that nature can nuzzle a crop for
months with moisture and warm sunshine,
then slap it unmercifully in a few violent
moments. Or she can bring it to a
wonderful, record harvest—causing farmers
to breathe a thankful sigh of relief that
the crop is in the bin.

Working with the partnership of water and the sun, farmers can grow almost anything in America—somewhere. The size and diversity of our nation's agriculture make our food supply almost disaster-proof. However, local drought, hail, floods, blizzards, and early or late frosts almost wipe out some farmers every year. Farmers' annual operating expenses are so high that the loss of a season's crop—and income—is a personal tragedy.

O'REAR

Thunderstorms can bring welcome relief
and needed rain. Yet they can be awesome
as they grow and loom fiercely overhead,
as in Brawley, California.

This sharp crack of lightning near
Kankakee, Illinois, was a harmless though
brilliant display of nature. But the next one
might start a hay barn on fire, or kill cattle
in their stanchions. In the West, lightning
is a main cause of forest fires.

PHOTOGRAPHED BY OLSON

Above
Water was higher than his head where Joe E. Bartholomay trudges back to his farmyard after a flood. The cleanup job on his dairy farm near Leonard, North Dakota was massive.

Opposite page
The Red River Valley—40 to 60 miles wide—is known as the Nile of the North, not because of seasonal floods but rather because of its black fertile soil.

Disastrous floods cause havoc somewhere every year. When water rose in the Red River Valley of North Dakota and Minnesota, it covered hundreds of farms and millions of acres of some of the world's richest farmland. Damage ran into *billions* of dollars. Said a resident, "Problem is the land is so level you can stand on a soft drink can and see from one end of the Valley to the other. There's just no place for the water to go."

Ranching is working out in weather that
can soak you or freeze you or dry you up
like a prune. On a hot day in the field
there's nothing quite like a cool drink, as
Norman Pape of Wyoming can attest.

When a farm family of nine is outfitted to
work in the weather, it . . . well, that's a lot
of clothes to keep in order.

DEVORE

Winter brings a mixture of feelings on the farm. Blizzards, drifting snow, and frigid winds take their toll of livestock on the range—and slow down gains on animals in the feedlot. Yet the snow which piles up on mountain ranges supplies next summer's irrigation water. Snow also provides a blanket, and needed moisture, for winter wheat. Sub-zero temperatures kill overwintering insects, reducing next season's damage. Winter is a time to plan for the coming crop season; go to meetings; read up on new techniques; and get up a little later in the morning. Whatever weather comes, farmers have learned to live with it; and never tire of discussing it, since weather is more than a curiosity or an inconvenience —it is the lifeblood of farming around which all else is organized.

Come snow, sleet or rain, livestock have
to eat. That can mean getting to them
through the deep snow, as on the
LaVaughn Herrick ranch, Cascade, Idaho.
Sometimes after heavy blizzards "hay
drops" from planes are needed to feed
cattle in remote sections.

A snowmobile gives Howard Gestrin a new
mobility in the deep winter snow in Idaho.
He can now check his cattle with ease.

F armers can't think of one nice thing to say about hail. Especially in Montgomery County, Maryland, after the storm that struck in July 1975. That day, at about 4:30 p.m., the sky turned green, and the hailstorm hit. It devastated a strip 4 miles wide and 10 miles long. While it completely riddled crops on one side of the road, it freakishly left those on the other side unscathed.

On the Hollis E. Hopkins farm in Maryland, the July hailstorm ruined 35 acres of ripened wheat. Hollis estimated the fields would have yielded 60 bushels an acre of wheat selling for more than $3 a bushel.

Hail ripped through peach flesh on 1,000
trees owned by Forest Hough in Maryland.

Tornadoes, nature's most violent storm, are common only in Australia and the United States. Observed in all parts of the U.S., they strike most often in the Midwest. Killer tornadoes leave a path of unbelievable destruction, with loss of lives and damage in the millions of dollars.

In June, 1975, a tornado swept down on the Harold Bick farm, five miles west of Farnam, Nebraska. The two wheat trucks were tossed a hundred yards from their parking spots. An expensive combine suffered the same fate. Two buildings were smashed; bits and pieces of one building were found five miles away.

First a tornado, then floods struck the
Karmen Miller farm in extreme west-central
Minnesota in June 1975. The tornadic
winds splintered trees and collapsed a bin
of stored soybeans.

Nature may appear to be fickle and
unpredictable. Yet there is a certainty
about her. In some sections, such as the
Great Plains, you know that drouths will
come—you just don't know when. Maps
printed in 1820-1850 called the Great Plains
the Great American Desert. Yet at times
this area can pour out bumper crops of
wheat. In 1973 Seward County, Kansas, had
a big wheat crop—in the winter of 1975-76
dry winds were blowing young wheat
plants right out of the ground.

First it was a moderately dry fall in the
San Joaquin Valley of California in 1975.
Then it turned really dry. December 1975
and January 1976 were the driest on record
for those months—less than one-quarter of
an inch of rain for the two months at
Fresno. Then came relief. In February,
Fresno got 4.72 inches of rain. Snowpacks
in the mountains increased, promising
irrigation water for later. A rainbow seemed
appropriate.

Nature is stingy with good weather, so farmers must make every minute count when it's time to plant, spray, cultivate, hay, or harvest. When the grain is ripe, the combines must run late, and in the spring when the time is right to plant, farmers work into the night.

SPECIAL EVENTS

Overleaf   PHOTOGRAPHED BY DAILEY

One thing about waiting for a parade in a small town—you know you're going to recognize most of the people in the parade. Chances are good they'll be related to you. It's fun to call out at a big sister strutting in front of the high school band to see if she'll blush. Wonder what Ed will look like this year? It takes only a few minutes to walk or drive to a good spot along the parade route . . . another few minutes to get home afterward. They have chairs for spectators at the Clio Fall Festival in Iowa.

Farm people celebrate their accomplishments with a variety of special events, many of them traditional affairs held year after year, "as long as anyone can remember." Weather, crop conditions, and livestock prices are invariably topics of conversation. Farmers also exchange ideas and pass along production tips.

Opposite page
There comes a time in every fair visit
when sitting down is the thing to do—
preferably in the shade.

Banquets and other special dinners are a
regular part of a farm family's life.
Associations of farmers with common
interests, such as Illinois farmers who
breed Berkshire hogs, meet annually or
more often to talk over the state of the
art. Such meetings provide an
opportunity to get away from the farm
if only for awhile.

There's a lot of pride in farming . . . pride that is fed continuously by competition . . . competition that is mental—getting the most out of the marketplace, out of the animals and machines you work with—and competition that is outright physical. Long hard work builds up muscles that strain to be tested. Frontier wrestling was part of the tradition. So have been horse races and horse pulling contests. Nowadays tractor

pulling contests have been booming in popularity. In
a horse pulling contest, horses are skillfully urged to pull
heavily-weighted stone boats or sleds representing plows or
heavy wagon loads. Weights are piled on after each
effort until the horse finally fails to pull the load. Tractors
pull against a steadily increasing load that finally stalls
the engine or makes the wheels spin uselessly.

During July and August last year there were 34 sanctioned tractor pulls in 10 states and the prize money exceeded $250,000. There were 4,500 members in a national tractor pullers' association last year, compared with just 150 in 1969. Farmers with field tractors are still in many of the contests but people with tank engines, airplane engines and even jet engines are pulling in the contests too. There are three main classes for tractors: farm stock, superstock and modified, with further categories according to weight. Farmers will fine tune their engines, perhaps even make some other adjustments in their farm shops, then put on tires that are about half worn out and adjust the hitch to the best advantage before heading for the contest. The idea is to apply the most horsepower in the lightest machine that can provide adequate traction.

The Hulett (Wyoming) Roping Club's
annual steak fry attracts more than
1,000 people from Wyoming, Montana and
South Dakota. They turn out for good
food and hearty fun—which includes a
rodeo. J. D. Proctor lost his hat and is
about to lose his seat on
the back of a bull.

The Missouri State High School Rodeo
Clinic, in Greencastle, offers
broncobusting, bull riding and calf
roping. They refer to it as the
three R's of high school rodeo: ridin',
ropin', and rubbin' alcohol. Missouri
has had High School Rodeo for 20 years,
but this clinic, with rodeo professionals
as instructors, was new last year.

Opposite page
Sam Shuey is proud that he has taken care of his animal for months. Now he's going to prove how good he is at it—at the Ohio State Fair. Like thousands of other youngsters in 4-H and Future Farmers of America programs, he's learned a lot about farming while raising his animal . . . learned a lot about life, such as responsibility. Now it all boils down in the show ring. Both Sam and his animal are ready.

Livestock breeders like to compare their best animals with the best animals of other breeders. The ultimate test is in the records—the quality and quantity of progeny—but breed shows that compare individual animals in terms of the latest desirable characteristics have strongly influenced the continuing improvement of breeds. Breeders are always trying to upgrade their stock animals. They attend show after show, exhibit after exhibit, in hopes of finding a better animal to buy. Or, there may be an opportunity to sell some animals to other breeders.

Berkshire hog breeders have been organized in the U.S. since 1875. Shows and sales at the centennial conference of the American Berkshire Association in Springfield, Illinois drew the same intense interest as in past years.

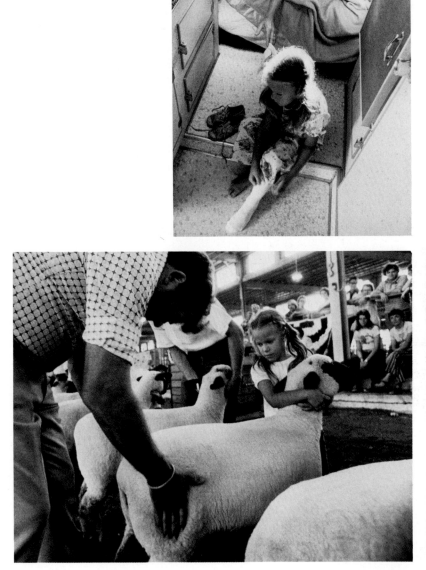

PHOTOGRAPHED BY BAER

You have to get up early in the morning if you plan to stick with 6-year-old Heidi Evans when she's showing sheep at the Ohio State Fair. During the day she'll feed and water her prize lambs, and watch hopefully as they're judged in the show ring. The daughter of Mr. and Mrs. DeWitt Evans, of Jamestown, Ohio, Heidi—like her sheep—comes out a winner.

Below
Wendy Morrison leads the high school
band through Limon, Colorado, during
the Harvest Festival parade.

In the Fall, many rural communities hold special events.
Limon, Colorado, is typical. Besides the Harvest
Festival parade there is a fly-in by the area's flying
farmers and ranchers, a cricket race, a tail-wagging
contest among pet dogs, food galore, and a melodrama
performed inside a large farm storage structure.

Opposite page
Indian boys join with adults during
the Harvest Dance, a variation of a
corn dance. "A dance is a prayer, and
this dance is a prayer of thanks for a
good harvest," they explain. Ceremonies
take place at San Ildefonso, New Mexico.

Like so many small towns in rural
America, the heartbeat of Norborne,
Missouri is its farm trade. The community
observed the Bicentennial with a
special flag ceremony, as the high
school band played and the Lutheran
Church choir sang. Officials who
spoke included a congressman and
the state's lieutenant governor.

119

The tune is familiar. Grandma used to
sing it softly while she rocked in her
chair. It was about young lovers and
something terrible happening to them.
It was hard to imagine Grandma was
young . . . even in love . . . maybe
silly sometimes. The man with the
fiddle, Carl Sorensen, knows the tune.
He remembers. The folks in Limon,
Colorado remember, too . . .
and tap their toes.

Any good reason will do for a little fun. The annual Hobo Dance of the B-Lo-C (Below Sea) square dance club is held on April 15, to "commemorate" the date when taxes must be paid. Event is staged in El Centro, California.

The Jackson Grange Fair, in Jackson,
Maine, includes two events that farm
kids and grown-ups never seem to
tire of: apple-dunking and horseshoes.

The women's sack race is just part of
the fun at the Fall Festival in Clio, Iowa.
Such small town events are often
called "homecomings." There's a parade,
tractor pull, bubblegum blowing
contest, horseshoes, and foot races.
First place in all events at Clio
is a "crisp, new dollar bill."

It was predictable that the second
annual Piedmont Market Hog and Trade
Show in Farmville, Virginia would include
a greased pig contest and ham raffle
in the afternoon. At lunch, the Virginia
Porkettes had offered porkburgers and
sausage sandwiches while supper
was to feature pork barbecue.

H ard work can take you a long way. The Mills County (Iowa) 4-H Club ran the refreshment stand at the county fair, held bake sales, and conducted other money-making ventures so the club would have enough cash for a week-long trip to Washington, D.C. In the nation's capital, the 4-H youth and their sponsors toured the city and saw the sights, and posed on the Capitol steps for a photograph with their congressman. Much like the thousands of other farm people who visit Washington annually, the young Iowans were thrilled with what they saw, but "it was good to get back home."

Queen contests are held in every section of the country, and in most instances honor a certain commodity or product raised by farmers and ranchers in that area. The queen contest is often the highlight of a special event. In Crowley, Louisiana the commodity was rice and the queen was Patricia Ann Cran, flanked by Sally Wilson, and Glenda Davis, runners-up. In Imperial County, California Paula McConnell reigned as queen of the annual Farm Bureau picnic.

Something about antique farm machinery
fascinates young and old alike. Old
thresher reunions attract bigger crowds
than ever before, and these colossal
steam-driven engines recall a time when
agriculture was just beginning to flex
its muscles. Today tractors half the size
do ten times the work, but they don't
hold the romance of the old-time
machines. Maybe someday they will,
as they, too, become antiques.

Rural Americans celebrated the nation's
Bicentennial in a thousand different ways.
In Roseberry, Idaho, Mrs. Ted Burgess
lit the candle on the "Happy Birthday,
U.S.A." cake, and joined others of the
community who caught the spirit with
covered wagon rides and clothing of
yesteryear, at their annual Bean Bake.

WHITE

Patriotism is a serious thing for rural
Americans, who love and respect their
nation's flag and what it represents.
Their ancestors hacked a nation out of a
wilderness. In this flag ceremony in Hulett,
Wyoming, the town's youngest citizen,
Will Mahoney, and its oldest citizen,
Mrs. Della Grant, presented
the Stars and Stripes.

Farmers and ranchers still work hard
and put in long hours even though
they have modern machinery. Perhaps
that's why they enjoy their local
community get-together so much, or the
state fair. The midway with its gaudy
lights and whirling rides offers thrills for
the young and memories for the old.

BUSINESS OF FARMING

Overleaf PHOTOGRAPHED BY DOWNIE
A fisheye lens 40 feet above carousels for cows in Norco, California, captures the mode of modern milking . . . modifying bovine behavior to the demands of sanitary, efficient mass production. Cows are washed by rotating sprinklers, herded toward a carousel by an automated gate, finally are milked and fed in a carousel.

Above
Ken Horn works on the farm books while his wife, Roberta, prepares supper in their Plymouth, Maine, home. Most farmers, or their wives, keep their own farm income, expense and tax records.

F arming is the nation's biggest business. The operators of the 2.8 million farms, their family labor, and hired help make up 4.4 million farmworkers—more workers than in the transportation, steel and automobile industries combined. One farmworker now supplies enough food and fiber for 56 people, up from 19 only 20 years ago. Output per farmworker is increasing at three times the rate in industry. The food shows up in the supermarket in 6,000 to 8,000 different forms. Farmers produce 53 percent more crops on 6 percent fewer acres than did their fathers. Now less than 5 percent of the population, farm people produce enough food to make Americans better fed, for less of their incomes, than anywhere else in the world. There's enough more to make us the world's largest agricultural exporters, supplying more than half of the feed grains and nearly half the wheat moving across international boundaries, and 70 percent of the soybeans. In 1975 we exported about $22 billion of agricultural products, $12 billion more than we imported. With the balance, we bought much-needed petroleum, important minerals, and consumer goods vital to the level of living of American consumers.

136

Farming provides the largest group of independent businessmen in America. They provide their own labor, finances, skills, marketing and management. The family lives at the business and shares the work. If they do well, they all prosper; if they fail, they all suffer. They seldom brag, because they know that things which look great today can look bad tomorrow as a result of weather, disease, insects or a falling market. Out of it comes a humility, a deep faith, a readiness to accept disappointment, and a reluctance to admit that things are going well.

To get the maximum results from pesticides applied to a field, Carlton Garner of North Carolina participates in an Extension Service pest management program. Douglas Peedin (above) records the number of insects in the field based on a sampling technique. Using this information, the Extension Service advises Garner on the amount and frequency of pesticide applications. The program saves farmers money and reduces environmental contamination.

Opposite page
With computer printouts, Extension Service farm management specialist Douglas Duey, right, helps Wayne Nielsen of Lincoln, Nebraska, analyze his cash flow and overall farm business situation.

Business talk among farmers and ranchers is mostly informal, down-to-earth. While waiting for lunch, Walter Bracht and his son-in-law Joe Gaddy stretch out on the floor to discuss the moisture content of the wheat Bracht had just delivered to the elevator. Salesman Bob Vechtel and Harry Doyle (right, bottom photo) stop off at the farm office of Ken Mowry and his father, Clarence, at Roaring Spring, Pennsylvania. Just as some businessmen frame the first dollar they make, Tom Mertensmeyer has samples of his first crops on the wall of his office at Carrollton, Missouri.

The oval door of a 30,000-bushel grain bin
at an Illinois equipment show frames a
discussion. Much farm business is
conducted on personal word. It's a
matter of great pride that a man is
as good as his word; no written
contract needed.

The farmstead buildings are the heart of the farm business, especially if it's a livestock farm like the John Derksen and Sons farm near South Bend, Indiana. There are barns to house the livestock, machine sheds to protect machinery, circular bins for grain, and silos for silage made from the corn (foreground). Farmers had an average of $184,545 assets per farm in 1975. Nearly three-fourths of that, $131,733, was tied up in real estate.

Non-real estate assets per farm averaged $8,716 in livestock and poultry, $19,791 in machinery and motor vehicles, $8,225 in crops stored on and off the farm, $5,473 in household equipment and furnishings, $5,342 in deposits and currency, $1,536 in U.S. savings bonds, and $3,729 in investment in cooperatives. Since so much money is tied up in production, farming is a business where you can live poor all your life and die rich.

Right

A feed console operator watches a television monitor to see when a truck is in position to receive its load of computer-calculated feed ingredients. She releases the ingredients into the truck and tells the operator by radio which pen gets the feed. The feed is mixed in the truck on the way to the animals.

A computer, television monitors, and human judgment play key roles in the huge feedlot meat "factory" that is Monfort of Colorado, Inc. at Greeley, Colorado. As many as 250,000 head of cattle can be fed at one time in the unusually large operation. The Monfort firm buys feeder steers weighing about 650 to 850 pounds each at auctions and from farmers and ranchers. When Monfort is through feeding them a least-cost ration determined by a computer, they average 1,175 pounds each. About 90 percent of them are graded USDA Choice. Only about one percent of U.S. farms are corporations, and 9 out of 10 of them are family-type corporations formed to pass the farm from one generation to the next.

Separate pens of beef cattle fill acres of Colorado countryside at the Monfort operation. Private roads for trucks to bring feed and haul cattle away to market interlace the pens. The animals in each pen are nearly all the same age and stage of development so that they can be marketed at the same time. This separation also helps keep other records, such as weight gain.

Imposing as an aircraft carrier on the prairie, Elevator B of Far-Mar-Co., Inc., Hutchinson, Kansas, is only 67 feet short of a half-mile long. Its 1,099 bins are 127 feet tall. Yet its capacity of 18 million bushels of wheat represents the production of only three Kansas wheat counties in a bumper year. Far-Mar-Co. is a federated cooperative—it is owned by farmer cooperatives which, in this case, are owned by more than 300,000 farmers.

A fter food and fiber leave the farms, they must get to you in your local store in a form you can use. Agriculture needs the services of 8 to 10 million people to process, transport, store, and merchandise the output of the Nation's farms. For example, the baking industry, including plants for making bread, biscuits and crackers, employs a quarter million workers and has a payroll of $2.3 billion. Cotton mills and finishing plants employ 152,000 workers and have payrolls of almost $1 billion. Investments of the cooperatives and corporations in food and fiber processing and marketing run into many billions of dollars. Packaging and transportation alone cost about $20 billion a year. About 60 per cent of the consumer cost of food is added after it leaves the farm.

Opposite Page
This gin in Tunica County, Mississippi, bales as much cotton in an hour as a mechanical cotton picker can harvest in a day. It separates cotton fiber from the cotton seed, then cleans it for textile processing. Machines press the cotton into ultra-compact bales weighing about 500 pounds and wrap them in plastic for extra protection.

Tank truck deliveries of scientifically
formulated feed save farmers large on-site
investments in feed storage and mixing
facilities. The feed arriving at the Bateman
farm in West Jordan, Utah, is a premixed,
high-nutrient pelletized feed. It's unloaded
into a hopper car, which, in turn is
emptied into feeding troughs.

BAER

Tractor tires are a high cost item in the modern farmer's budget. Tires like these retail for $1,000 to $1,200 each. For a heavy vehicle with eight wheels, that's a possible investment of $9,600.

Will it pay to buy tubing to drain a piece of land? Farmers always face the question: Will it pay? How soon? How long will it tie up the money? Will it pay better to put on another $500 of fertilizer, or put the money in pesticides? Sell the corn or buy feeder pigs? Farmers are walking computers always balancing one choice against another.

You have to stay flexible. When competition from the South made raising and dressing poultry unprofitable for Wisconsin farmer Ben Turzinski, he started buying dressed broilers in Alabama and selling them in Wisconsin. He contracts to truck the broilers north; owns five refrigerated trucks for local distribution. He also grows corn on 500 acres, shells it, dries it and sells it to local dairymen. He contracts to raise snap beans on another 500 acres. "We raised nine children on this land," Turzinski adds. His four sons are in the business with him.

150

When it is 30 miles to the nearest town, a plane can be mighty useful—for buying replacement parts, getting someone to a doctor, going to a field day, finding cattle after a storm, and dozens of other things. There are 10,000 members of International Flying Farmers—which includes principally the U.S., Canada and Mexico. About 50 farmers and ranchers from remote areas of Colorado flew into Limon, Colorado, (population 1,800) for the community's annual Harvest Festival in 1975.

Communication keeps the machinery of any business operating. At morning coffee, all hands at the Russ Jeckel farm in Illinois get a chance to plan the day. The weather may change the plan, so you have to "stay loose." A key member of the team, Mary Jeckel, handles the books. The "team," left to right, Laverne Debatin, Russ Jeckel, Greg Nelson, John Boudeman, John Jeckel (Russ's father), and John Deuth, a student trainee on the 500-acre corn/hog farm. Opposite, Jeckel listens to Mike Still, agriculture teacher at Illinois Central College, which sends trainees to work with Jeckel.

PHOTOGRAPHED BY KUYKENDALL

S ome farmers sell their products directly to the
customer. It's not new—it's as old as farming itself—
but somewhat uncommon today. Mr. and Mrs. George
R. McCoy specialize in fresh sweet corn and other
vegetables on their 20-acre Jackson, Mississippi,
farm. The McCoys take in $8–10,000 a year. This
kind of farming takes hard work, long hours, sales
know-how and overall good management.

PHOTOGRAPHED BY WARREN

Overleaf and above   PHOTOGRAPHED BY BAER

BRILL

Under the open skies of Malta, Illinois, the Farm Progress Show in 1975 drew as many as 100,000 people a day for three days. They came to see first hand, how the latest farm machinery, equipment, chemicals and other technological improvements worked on real soil and real crops. It was a great day for agricultural comparison shoppers.

National and international shows and exhibits provide opportunities for farmers to see the latest tools of their business. Sometimes a farmer turns over his land for the exhibition of machinery and demonstration of new seeds and equipment. Farmers drive long distances or fly in to see how new machines operate under field conditions. Folks come from overseas to observe and buy. There are about 4,000 county, state and other major farm shows in the U.S. each year.

Japanese were among those attending and buying at the National Barrow Show in Austin, Minnesota, in September, 1975. The Japanese are building up their hog industry—an industry now small but expected to grow. That could increase opportunities for the sale of feed grains from the U.S. There are now more acres in the U.S. growing food for Japan than there are acres of farmland in Japan.

At the Farm Progress Show, farmers saw a
lot of horsepower at work—including an
unusual tractor that could cost $60–80,000,
depending on options and other features.
This behemoth was pulling 14 bottoms
(plow blades) with 636 horsepower
springing from twin diesel engines. It
weighed 20 tons.

Farmers are active in the leadership of their community—in their cooperatives, farm organizations, commodity groups, conservation societies, banks, churches, hospitals, schools and local government. They know the value of a dollar and hard work—wisdom gained from running their own farm businesses.

Besides operating his 300-cow dairy farm, Dale Bateman is a member of the High Council in the Church of Latter Day Saints of Jesus Christ at West Jordan, Utah.

Farmers are almost always willing to share their time and good ideas. In 1975, Dwain Adkinson, a beef cattle breeder at Raymondville, Missouri, was assistant vice president of his production credit association. His wife Polly taught art in a nearby elementary school. They opened their farm to the Young Farmers Tour so that others could see their plantings of caucasian bluestem grass for pasture.

Below

At 5 a.m. daily, Maine potato grower Larry Park watches the Potato Pickers TV Special while his wife Edith prepares breakfast. Farmers call the station to say whether they will be planting, harvesting or weeding that day, and the station passes on the information to work crews. The program also features market news, interviews with specialists, and goings-on around the farm community.

ROBINSON

DAILEY

F armers keep tuned into outside events in order to evaluate the effect on their production and marketing plans. Rural mass media beam a steady stream of business information directly at farmers. The weather and daily markets are a chief concern. How-to articles in magazines are read with keen interest. Successful farmers never stop trying to do the job better.

Listening to the noon market report is a ritual across the country, as it is for Herman White, tobacco farmer.

Opposite page

While other members of the family relax with a game of cards after a hard day's work, E. W. Raasch, Jr., reads a magazine to pick up new ideas from other farmers about hog breeding and grain growing.

164

Opposite page

Making beef takes patience—and time, as Bing Furnish knows when he moves Herefords, Angus, Charolais and other beef cattle out to pasture on the Hitch Ranch, Guymon, Oklahoma. Yearlings are kept on pasture until they weigh 6–700 pounds. Then they're brought in to a feedlot and fed to 1,000 to 1,100 pounds before slaughter. If long-range prospects look good, a cattleman may decide to enlarge his breeding herd and produce more meat—but it will be 4½ years before more beef shows up at the store. First, he keeps a heifer calf rather than let her be fed for slaughter; that reduces the beef supply that year. The heifer has her first calf as a two-year old. When that calf goes to market a year or two later, it replaces the beef supply lost when its mother was held back from slaughter. Her second calf is the first to increase the meat supply—14 to 24 months after it is born. Time elapsed from the decision to increase meat supplies: 4½ years or more.

T he U.S. is a strong livestock nation. Meat, milk and eggs are prominent in the national diet. Throughout the world people tend to move up from starchy foods to proteins as their levels of affluence improve. For example, 35% of the calories consumed in the U.S. are from animal products, compared with 32% in West Germany, 13% in Brazil, and 6% in India. Livestock have, over the years, worked well with crops on our family-type farms. Livestock largely were put out to pasture in the summer during the busy field work. The heavy chores of feeding and caring for animals came during the winter months when the family wasn't busy in the field. Now livestock farming is becoming specialized. More animals are confined year-round as the chores get more mechanized. It used to be said "the eye of the master fattens his cattle," indicating that feeding was an individual art; increasingly, rations and management systems are packaged. Still, a good farmer can simply walk among his livestock and sense whether things are going well.

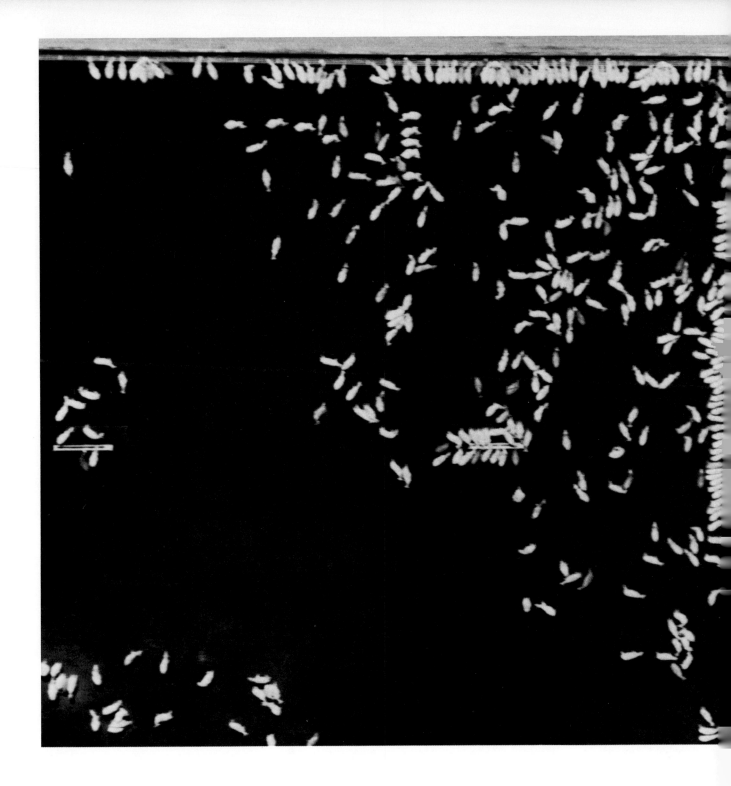

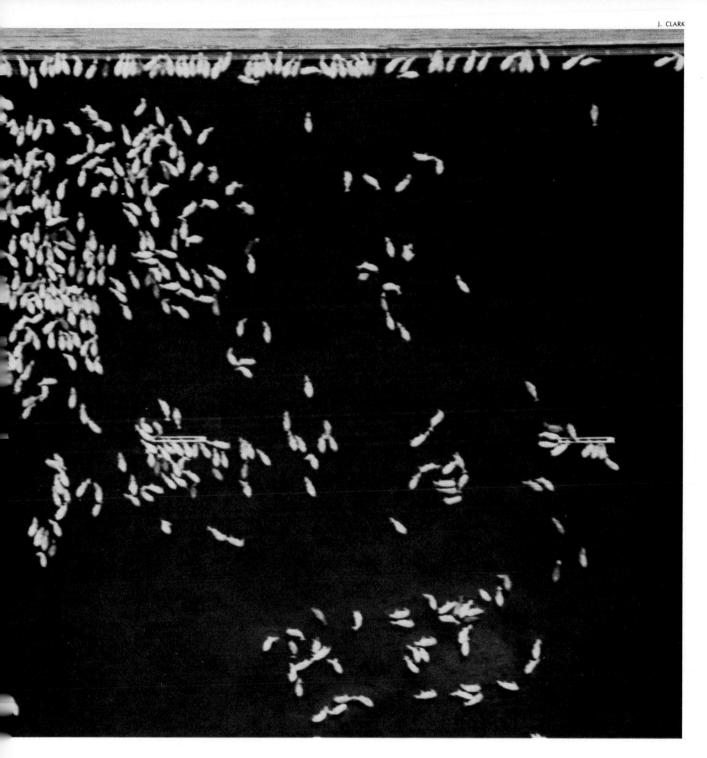

From afar, cattle look like ants in the pens of the Steve Marks Cattle Co. feedlot in Zamora, California. These feedlots are divided into pens where cattle of similar age and size are fed together. Cattle in each pen "graduate" together to market. Rations for cattle in big feedlots are scientifically formulated for proper balance of carbohydrates, fats, proteins, minerals, fiber and vitamins. As the costs of ingredients change, computers alter the mix to create least-cost rations. We know more about healthful livestock rations than we do about human diets.

Their food is delivered to them by chain feeder, their water is conveniently located in special containers, and their nests are just a few feet away. The breeder hens of Perdue, Inc. are pampered to lay as many eggs as possible in their Salisbury, Maryland, houses. The eggs will be hatched to become broiler chicks.

To meet rising labor costs and the need for greater efficiency, livestock often are confined in buildings and lots so feeding and watering can be automated. Waste disposal creates a costly problem. A feedlot of 1,000 cattle has a waste disposal problem equivalent to a town of 6,000 people.

Young farmers on a tour visit a 1,000-capacity hog finishing building astraddle a lagoon. The lagoon catches manure dropping through a slatted floor. This holds down odors. The slurry is used on fields as fertilizer, thus recycling nutrients into the soil.

This open confinement building for
feeding beef cattle was demonstrated at
the 1975 Farm Progress Show in Illinois.
Manure falls through a slatted floor into
a collection pit, where it may be pumped
into a wagon for spreading on fields. Or
it may be pumped directly into an
irrigation system.

Cowboys on motorcycles are becoming a common sight on some cow-calf operations. The George Landers farm at Dadeville, Missouri, raises Charolais cows and calves. Cow-calf herds on grazing land provide the beef calves that move into specialized feedlots for finishing. Three out of four pounds of the beef we eat comes from roughages.

Even though gutters behind dairy cows are scraped clean mechanically in stanchion barns, there's still lots of handwork for the entire family in spreading bedding and cleaning up. Lisa Marietti is going to lend a hand to grandfather Dominic Marietti in Chepachet, Rhode Island. Younger granddaughter Nicole will get her chance later.

March Lockhart, a graduate chemist, turned down a move to the big city and a promotion in order to stay on his farm in El Dorado, Arkansas. He was reared in the city, became interested in farming through a high school friend. He and his wife Pat work at regular jobs but raise Berkshire hogs and Tennessee Walking Horses part-time on their farm.

BOGRE

H ogs have probably paid for more farms than any other single farm product, hence the term "mortgage lifters." Hogs are raised in every state, but most of them are in the Midwest near the corn and soybeans which make up the bulk of their feed. Hog prices go up and down in cycles. With too many hogs, the price goes down, and farmers cut back production. This results in less pork, the price of hogs goes up, and farmers raise more. It's seemingly as endless and inevitable as the tide. Geneticists and breeders have remade the hog from a chubby, short, lardy animal to a long, heavily-muscled chap with larger, leaner pork chops and bigger hams. The average amount of lard per 240-pound hog has declined from 29 pounds in 1960 to 12 pounds now. Lean cuts in a hog carcass—such as pork chops, hams and loins—have increased from 37 percent of the carcass in 1960 to 50–55 percent today.

You can get a tan for the weekend
swimming party even while feeding hogs.
The hogs could care less as long as you
get back on time to feed them again.
Livestock and chores go together like ham
and eggs. Chores and farm youngsters are
also a pair. Chores build responsibility,
versatility, humility, dependability, and a
lot of other virtues—often not
acknowledged by the youngster until
20 years later.

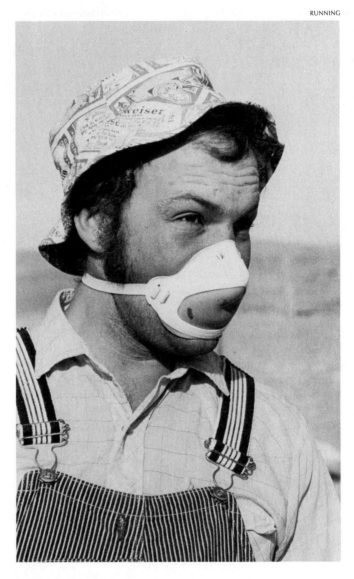

Raising poultry is big business where birds are handled in huge batches with amazing efficiency. Most of the broiler business is vertically integrated. The broiler chicks and the feed are owned by a firm which contracts with the farmer to feed them in his broiler houses. The farmer is paid a set amount per pound of broiler meat, and he gets a bonus if he does a good job. It takes about 7½ weeks to raise a 4-pound broiler on 7.6 pounds of feed. Meantime, poultry breeders have developed birds with more meat on the legs and breasts. With this efficiency, poultry has moved from a Sunday treat to an everyday place in the diet.

Easily frightened and stampeded, turkeys
are moved gently down a slight slope,
urged on by burlap sacks. They'll soon be
on their way to market.

Automatic waterers and a moving chain of
feed seem to stretch into infinity. The
height of both are adjusted as chicks
grow larger in the big broiler houses of
Bill Swilley in El Dorado, Arkansas.

Opposite Page
Moving turkeys in Utah in October is dry
dusty business so masks such as that worn
by Tracy Cook are almost necessary.

BOGRE

179

M ilk has nourished the nation. The baby's formula and the carton of milk start here where dairying is one of the most demanding jobs in farming. The cows have to be milked morning and night 365 days a year, including Saturdays and Sundays. No shutting off the cows for a couple of days' vacation. Labor is hard to get for that job, expensive to keep; so dairying remains largely a family enterprise averaging 25 cows. Buildings and equipment must meet health standards, and the investment may easily run $1,800 per cow. In an effort to keep up with rising costs, dairymen have increased average milk production from 5,314 pounds per cow in 1950 to 10,354 in 1975 through better feeding and management, and artificial insemination which brings a good sire within reach of every dairyman. In sophisticated herds, computers select the best matings from characteristics of blood lines.

Heroines of the Heizer farm in Middlebrook, Virginia are the 160 Brown Swiss and Holstein cows which move through the farm's sophisticated rotary milking parlor twice daily to be milked. Giving milk is a delicate physiological function triggered by hormones. Appropriately, cows are fed well, kept comfortable and calm, and treated gently. Most dairymen know their cows by name or number and speak gently to each one during the mechanized milking.

DOWNIE

Future milk producers—Holstein calves—
on the John Leal farm, Norco, California
are brought their daily ration of
pulverized alfalfa by Catarino Llamas.
Youngest calves are fed cows' milk; later
cows' milk mixed with pulverized alfalfa;
and finally, grain as they get older. Calves
are often started in pens up off the ground
to keep them clean and healthy.

The system of milking used by dairymen depends somewhat on the number of hands available to help. Michelle, one of 10 children on the Ray DePriest farm at Palmer, Alaska, takes the milking machines to the cows. Machines are attached to an airtight pipeline leading to a cooling tank. In another system, cows take turns moving into a milking parlor where the dairyman is in a pit and works machines at chest level.

Part of the pipeline milking system on the Norland-Rowbotham farm in Walworth, Wisconsin, is a receiver jar filling with milk fresh from a cow. It will automatically empty into the pipeline when full. Pipelines and jars are flushed and cleaned after each milking. Regular bacteria counts are taken to assure that sanitation is adequate.

Question: Would you rather have the milk
the tank truck can hold (38,000 pounds of
it) or the milk that the cow can produce
in a year? Pick the cow's production—it
was 50,759 pounds in 1974. That's nearly
24,000 quarts. The average milk cow
delivers about 10,000 pounds a year. But
this cow from Mowry Farms in
Pennsylvania was the first to top 50,000
pounds. Yet an Indiana cow topped her
record in 1975. You need the right
genes for that.

Sheep can't be surpassed at converting what would be wasted roughage into wool and meat. But sheep raising has its problems. In farm areas sheep-killing dogs can mangle a flock overnight. In range areas, wild predators feast on lamb. Besides, sheep herding on the range is a lonely life and the number of people willing to adopt it is declining. So are the number of sheep, dropping from 30 million sheep and lambs in 1950 to 14½ million in 1975. Range sheep move and munch from winter to summer pastures, accompanied by men who spend six or seven months virtually alone moving the flock from one grazing area to another. Basque shepherds of Northern Spain and Southern France played a major role in establishing the Western sheep industry. Among today's Basque shepherds are Jean Etchamendy (above), owner of the Etchamendy Sheep Company, who continues to work the trail after 25 years because of the difficulty in hiring shepherds. With a shepherd's crook and a lamb he has saved is Jose Aleman (opposite). Lonely and homesick, he returned to his native Spain after this drive.

PETERSON

Cattle move down the highway on a Sunday in California. The beef business is a mixture of new and old. Cowboys on horses still herd and work single animals for branding, medical treatment, and the like. But cattlemen use pickup trucks, motorbikes, snowmobiles, even helicopters to look after their herds. There are short drives to pasture and at roundup time. Trucks are used to haul animals long distances to pasture, feedlots or packing houses. Open range still exists in many places, but fenced herds are common. Breeding management may consist of an available bull or include artificial insemination, computers, and weight-for-age records.

In the fall, cattle that have been on the open range in Montana are brought in for winter pasture near ranch headquarters. By whooping and hollering, such as Gary Mills of the TEE Bar Ranch is doing, cowhands separate calves to check them out for physical condition and weighing. Cowboy pay ranges widely; many receive wages, room and board and often run cattle under their own brand along with the employer's herd.

Out on pasture at the Ira D. McClurkin Farm in Montgomery County, Alabama, a reluctant cow nears the end of the trail when McClurkin and two hands, Elijah Clayton and Alex Robinson, arrive to take her back to the farmyard. There are days when nothing is as cantankerous as an animal that doesn't want to do what you want it to.

PHOTOGRAPHED BY WRIGHT

Branding is still necessary to identify cattle, especially in open range where the cattle of several ranches may be mixed. Even within one ranch, more than one brand may be required. On the Pape Ranch at Daniel, Wyoming, there are three brands: one for the corporation, one for the animals that Norman Pape runs, and another for those run by John "Peck" May, a hand on the ranch. First the branding irons are heated on the fire . . .

. . . then the calves are flipped for the branding. These calves are larger than usual for branding because they were missed in the spring roundup and brought in during fall roundup.

Finally, there is the actual branding operation. Branding offers protection against rustling, which is still a problem in the West. Hijackers even pick up livestock from pastures in farm communities across the country.

A working cow horse is a cattleman's best assistant. This one will keep the rope taut until Leroy Tillotson and Lawrence Kock of Farnam, Nebraska, have finished administering an antibiotic for the bull's infected leg. Most cattlemen have some knowledge of preventive medicine from experience, courses in college, or through the Extension Service. They know, too, when it's time to bring in one of the nation's 29,000 veterinarians. Keeping the nation's livestock and poultry healthy costs farmers $400 million a year.

Youngsters learn fast on a ranch.
David watches his father, Norman Pape,
prepare to inoculate calves for blackleg.

Young cow emerges from
specially-designed holding chute after
being checked by veterinarian Dr. David
Bisbee for pneumonia and pregnancy. She
also was weighed and given shots
following a summer on the range. Just
part of the fall roundup on the TEE Bar
Ranch in Montana.

Show rings such as at the Nebraska State Fair in Lincoln are more than beauty contests. Judges "look under the skin" for the cuts of meat that consumers want, and watch for weakness that might impair the animal's ability to produce. Youngsters learn to select good livestock, put together an efficient ration, and bring the animal up to the day of the show in tip-top "bloom" condition. Less

attention is paid to the physical appearance of livestock
these days and more to performance—such as
weight-for-age, feed per pound of gain, and carcass
cut-out. These are indications that a bloodline can
perform under normal conditions, make money for
a commercial operator, and turn out the kind of
product the market wants.

BAER

Pride of ownership comes through
especially at show time. Sam and
Robert Shuey groom prize Hereford they
showed at the Ohio State Fair.

Opposite Page
There is a very special relationship
between farmers and ranchers and the
animals they work with, and it shows.
Chuck Smith of Farmington, New Mexico
won first place for his California breed
rabbit at the San Juan County Fair.

The fast-paced action of a livestock sale can be a lively show to watch. Someone in the grandstands winks or nods or tugs his ear and one of the ringmen waves and shouts "I've got a 45" or "I've got a 63" (meaning $4,500 or $6,300) and the auctioneer—Col. Jewett Fulkerson—announces the bidding for the Polled Hereford being led by Walter McKellar, ranch manager of the CMR Ranch, Senatobia, Mississippi. It's the annual picnic sale at the ranch—one of the well-known private sales in the beef industry. A one-fourth interest in a bull at the 1975 sale brought a top price of $12,000. Ranch owner M. P. "Hot" Moore has held 34 consecutive annual sales.

Above
Ringman Wesley Hayes shouts a prospective buyer's bid to the auctioneer at the CMR sale. Results are worth shouting about. The average sale price at CMR might easily run $3,000 to $6,000 per animal, and once hit a record $7,965 per animal.

Right
Ringman Bobby Baker is caught up in the fever of the sale. There's a lot of pyschology to keeping the sale momentum going and the bids coming. A good auctioneer is an artist at it.

Men, women and youngsters attending such sales are intent on the bidding, constantly checking the sale catalog for the pedigree of the animal being auctioned. These animals are being sold for breeding—not slaughter—and their bloodlines, the performance of their dams, sires and earlier ancestors, govern their value. Ranch owner Moore says he likes to breed *out* the "middles" of a beef animal, which don't bring much at the meat market, and breed *in* the "rear ends" that provide bigger and better rump roasts, porterhouses and sirloins.

PHOTOGRAPHED BY WARREN

203

This Hampshire boar is being sold for breeding purposes at a private auction in Mahomet, Illinois. Good ancestry is important in hogs as well as in dairy and beef cattle. Farmers look for lean, heavily muscled hogs that will gain fast, produce more meat

from less grain, have big litters and stay
healthy. That kind will make money
and produce the meat consumers want.
Farmers will come from across the
state to bid for them. It doesn't have
to be daylight to conduct business,
as the Lyle Bidner Hog Sale indicates.

Overleaf   PHOTOGRAPHED BY SCHUMAKER
Four generations of Wrights in Enosburg,
Vermont. Left to right: Melvin Wright,
his great-grandson Dean, 7, his son Donald
and Donald's wife Ruth (with Brenda
her granddaughter in front of her), Sharon,
9, Amy Sue, 2, and the young children's
parents, Carroll and Darlene Wright. For
them, Vermont is a land of "milk
and honey", since dairying and maple
sugaring are their way of life. Most
of today's farmers come from a line of
farm people that trails off into the
distant genealogical past.

F arm families are close to the fundamentals of life.
Births and death are continuous and obvious. So are
work, the earth and the weather, joy and a profound sense
of fulfillment. Freedom and independence—within the
limits imposed by Nature and the markets—are woven
into the fabric of American farm life. Farm life is work in
the field and caring for livestock. It's doing the chores and
cooking endless meals. It's coming home from school or
sitting in the shade of a vehicle to eat lunch. It's having
coffee with friends. When the wives aren't doing
housework they are often outdoors helping their
husbands. Sometimes they keep in touch by two-way
radio. For kids, the whole farm is a plaything. They can
drive tractors or play with a score of pets. Families not
only live together but work and play together. Farm
people go at life with a big auger. After all, what's life
about? Enjoy it a little.

Mail is a personal contact with the
world beyond the farm boundaries. Mail
for a lot of farmers, including the J. D.
Pembertons, includes a community
newspaper with an emphasis on family
and local news.

Chores—sometimes deadly dull, physical
but absolutely necessary—are a big part
of farm life, especially for youngsters.
Getting the cows lined up for milking is
one of the chores of Marsha Petty, 14.

Dean Wright, 7, of Enosburg, Vermont wrestles an empty milk can. He'll soon be doing chores with pride.

Right
It's one thing to pick cranberries, still another to get them to market. Mrs. Sam Schlegel and son, Brian, 5, of Long Beach, Washington are taking that first big step toward market together.

Farming is physical and meals are more
than a ritual. The family refuels and gets a
needed rest at mealtime. Mrs. Berrey and
her daughter, Debbie, clean up the kitchen,
while the menfolk are readying equipment
outside for a late evening's planting.

Pausing during a day of setting
(transplanting) tobacco plants, the Charley
Beaty family of Conway, South Carolina,
and their helpers take time for a noon
meal out of the sun. Left to right,
the diners are Jessie Bellamy, Larry
Young, Charley Beaty, Bernice Beaty,
his wife, and Charley Beaty, Jr.

GEORGIA

Ranch women are just as good cowboys as the regular ranch hands. Mrs. Robert Mosher was right in the middle of the TEE Bar Ranch roundup in Colorado from cutting cattle in the corral to keeping the cowboys fed from the back of the Mosher truckcamper. With her, left, were Larry Fleming, Frank Dellwo and her son Roland.

WILSON

Breaks are welcome when the people who work the land and livestock can fit them in. Often it's a food or water break—necessary to keep one's energy up for more hours in the sun. When the work is pressing, farmers and ranchers often take their food with them rather than drive back home to eat. But when they can relax, they like nothing better than a big picnic outdoors.

Combining wheat is hot work and a patch of shade at lunchtime is welcome. Seated in the shade of a truck during a break in the harvest on their farm near Colton, Washington are Gerry Schultheis, his father, Carroll and Gerry's grandfather, Jacob F. Schultheis.

214

Farmers call the Jif E-Mart on U.S. 83 near
La Feria, Texas their "country club." They
meet there for a morning break, swap
information and do business, all for the
price of a cup of coffee or a snack.

BOGRE

F arm women have been toughened in the forge of hard work. Yet, they retain their charming femininity. Perhaps more completely than in any other walk of life, they enjoy a complete partnership in their husband's business and way of life. They share the grinding work, the simple joys, the unutterable sorrows, the tough decisions and the fulfilling successes of life on the farm. They make tremendous sacrifices. Yet hardly any of them would trade their lot for anything in town. Well, maybe on some days they would—and would just as quickly want to be back.

Left
Modern farm wife Carole Lyons contacts her husband George by citizens band radio if something happens he should know about . . . perhaps an important phone call, piece of mail, or market report. She's part of a communication system that includes the home of George's brother, Bill, three cars (including that of a third brother, Ronnie), and a combine. Bill's wife, Mary, is a vital link in the chain.

Enchanted by her first year of farm life,
Kim Haas leans out the door to notify her
husband Davis of the birth of kittens. A
town girl, Kim was a high school
sweetheart of Davis, a farmer's son, and
married him in 1974. She moved into a
whole new kind of life, helping care for
1,300 chickens, 200 cattle, 140 hogs and
the kittens. She loves it.

Jean Schnelle keeps working, even when going into the yard to share a few words with husband Harold to ask when the men will be ready for dinner. Balancing six-months-old son Dwight on her hip, she manages to pull some weeds out of the planter. She's a true vice president in an apron.

Mowing the lawn is just one of the chores farm wife Edith Gaddy handles. Most of the day hers is the typical farm wife's fare of caring for the house, preparing meals, taking the children somewhere, or running to town for a spare part.

It's not unusual for Mrs. Berl Henry to lift 50-pound bags of shoat ration to fill the pig feeders. Taking care of livestock is second nature for some farm women, who are already busy taking care of children.

At the end of the day, or when weather grinds outdoor work to a halt, it's a chance to get some odd jobs out of the way. Gary Hansford called on his friends and had his hair cut by Mrs. Glen Patrick, the wife of a friend.

At night after a hard day's work and a
good dinner, Walter Bracht reads the
paper and watches television. Tomorrow
will be another tough day.

A spreader filled with clean straw is really a PT boat and your cousin Robert Bland is steering it and your brother Johnny Leal Jr., 4, is shooting down enemy aircraft with his slingshot. And you, Jimmy, 3, are looking to see where the crippled aircraft will fall.

Learning to be a wrangler can be a toughening experience. When calf and boy tangle, sometimes the calf wins.

Children never lack for things to do on the farm. There are as many chores as a body can handle. Parents see to that. The message seems to be: you might as well learn early that you have to work hard in life. Yet, knowing there is a lifetime of work ahead, farm parents are willing to let the children have some time to be just children. Then the whole farm is a plaything that can be endlessly subdivided into smaller playthings, which can be reassembled and built into different playthings. There are tractors and trucks to drive and a variety of pets to play with. There is school, of course, but when school is out and the chores are done, you can ride your own horse across the fields and feel the wind in your face. And you are free.

222

Roll out the barrel is only a sometime thing during potato harvest in Maine. Most of the time, those youngsters are filling the barrels with potatoes just dug out of the ground.

Family schedules and lives revolve around the school bus. Chores are undoubtedly waiting for Lisa and Frank McCann of Cascade, Idaho, but right now there's a puddle to be vaulted, or stepped in, depending on your mood.

It's great to be a farm girl with your own horse, and acres of open land. Mary Ann Martens of Anthony, Kansas, and her horse Taffy, blend together, exemplifying the spirit of the great outdoors that is the legend of rural America.

Farmers are tuned in wherever they are. Electronics takes care of that. Farmers in the most remote sections keep up on markets all over the world. They watch television news and judge for themselves about current events beyond their community concerns. The youngsters know all the latest song hits that the radio waves can handle.

Greg Hall takes music with him wherever he goes with an AM radio receiver he converted to handle both AM and FM. Observes Greg: "I don't know how anyone could stand driving a tractor all day without headphones."

226

Randall Jones finds guitar music pleasant company during the long days and nights of Alaska.

Family time is music making at the piano for Henry B. Perry, grandson Desmond Lowe, and brother-in-law Rozell Kendrick at their farm in Hardaway, Alabama.

227

Another farm is gone. The terminal ritual is an auction. The vibrancy that was a going farm, and a house filled with life and laughter, have been reduced to a few material items offered to the highest bidder. The auctioneer's sing-song chant is a familiar requiem in rural America as farmers retire, die or just "go away." The 2.8 million farms in 1975 are only half the number of 25 years ago. But change is inevitable. The farms that remain are larger, more prosperous, more durable. The loss of 22,000 farms nationally in 1975 was only one-tenth the decline in farm numbers in 1950.

Memorial Day is an important day for
respectful memories in rural America. The
Jack Roark family places flowers on a
grave in the Adams Cemetery.

Basic beliefs play a major role in farm
lives. Mrs. J. Brewer Bottorff pauses
beside a meaningful quotation. Nobody
can go through an endless chain of
farm births and growth and harvests—
and be subject to nature's mysteries,
bounty, and sometimes harshness—without
developing a philosophy of life.

The sun should always shine on weddings.
At the Hargis-Morton wedding on a
Saturday in June the reception line gathers
in the shade. Weddings top family events
as major occasions among close-knit
farm people.

When fire destroyed Ron and Jane
Nipple's dairy barn, near Millerstown, Pa.,
neighbors set aside several consecutive
Saturdays to rebuild their barn. The sturdy
oak timbers were home-grown.

Thanksgiving and apple butter just go together naturally when it's Fall in Virginia and there's plenty of both apples and turkeys. There's still a lot of preparin' to do (and paring, in the case of Billy Kipps, above). Helping Billy are other members of the Kipps family: Ward, Barbara and Luther. Part of making the apple butter is stirring the apples in a steaming cauldron outdoors. Waiting for the festive dinner to begin, Anne Kipps arranges plants by the window.

235

Finally there is Thanksgiving dinner— in one of the first states to celebrate that observance centuries before. Farm families—though they use modern management procedures and machinery— hold firmly to tradition. It's a feeling that comes with the land . . . along with spontaneous expressions of thanksgiving.

There are so many elements beyond the farmer's control which affect his livelihood and well-being. When the harvest is in and it's been a good one, then it's time to enjoy some of the fruits of the labor, and to be thankful, as the Kipps are doing. All America can be thankful for her abundance of food.

PERNOLD

HARVEST

Overleaf   PHOTOGRAPHED BY LUSTIG

America's modern miracle crop, soybeans, provides vital protein and oil for the U.S. and other countries. In the Thirties, two-thirds of the soybeans we raised were plowed under to improve the soil. By 1975, we'd learned to make soybeans far more valuable for human food and livestock feed. U.S. production had increased by 300 times; and the crop, valued at an incredible $7 billion, had become our No. 1 agricultural export. It is typical of the changing face of rural America.

H arvest is the payoff. Months after entrusting seed to the soil and the weather, after pouring costly nutrients into development of the plants, after fighting off strength-stealing weeds, and in many other ways nurturing life and health into his crop, the farmer looks anxiously for undeniable signs of maturity. Each crop makes its own unique demands upon its environment—the successful farmer is the one who knows these demands best and looks after them. His reward—his incentive from the beginning—

comes with the harvest. For U.S. farmers, the combined value of all crops harvested in 1975 was $55.7 billion— just one percent below the 1974 record of $56.4 billion. The corn harvest was valued at $14.38 billion; wheat at $7.4 billion; soybeans at $7 billion; cotton at $2.2 billion; grain sorghum at $1.8 billion; rice at $1.1 billion; hay at $6.5 billion; tobacco at $2.2 billion; potatoes at $1.5 billion, and sugarbeets at $800 million. Wheat, hay, tobacco and potato harvests set records.

Making hay while the sun shines is an expression that still has literal meaning on the farm. On Ken Walker's farm at Faribault, Minnesota, when the hay looks "right" and the weather is expected to remain fair for a few days, the hay is cut and left to dry—perhaps a day—then baled, loaded onto wagons and taken to the barn for storage.

Combines in the Palouse Hills of
Washington roll through a wheat field on
the Schultheis farm, cutting and threshing
in one operation. In earlier days wheat
was cut with a binder and set upright in
shocks by hand to keep the heads dry. On
threshing day, a crew pitched the bundles
onto a wagon, hauled them to the thresher,
and tossed them into the mouth of the
"separator." That system is now shown on
"old timers" day.

Mechanization of harvests, such as carrots
near Coachella, California makes it
possible for farmers to concentrate on
specialty crops and supply consumers with
fruits and vegetables year-round. This
carrot harvester enables two men to do
the work of 18, a key to quick harvesting
and economically priced food. Americans
get their food for less of their incomes
than anywhere else in the world.

W hen it's time to harvest, you need to keep rolling or lose the crop. Wheat farmers work into the night combining. Their grain is dry . . . so dry that a car's backfire could ignite it . . . so ripe that high winds and rain will knock it down and ruin its quality. Even when the crop is underground, as with potatoes, there is a right time and a wrong time to harvest. When potatoes are mature, they must be dug up and stored before they freeze. Maine potato harvesters work far past dark to get their crop in. Yet, frustratingly, they may have to delay their start in the morning until the ground and potatoes warm up. A potato that is too cold will bruise too easily in the harvesting process. Wheat farmers, also, must wait in the morning until the dew is off their crop before starting. You live in harmony with nature or fail.

Above

Larry Park, in cab, works past sundown to get the potatoes on his Presque Isle, Maine, farm harvested mechanically. Theoretically, round potatoes roll to one side of sloping conveyor belt while flat Maine stones stay put. People make sure it happens that way.

The wheat rolling out of the spout on the Ralph A. Hansen farm in Kingfisher, Oklahoma, may end up soon as a secretary's breakfast roll in Philadelphia. Or as a piece of life-saving bread for a child in India. U.S. farm exports, which hit $22 billion in 1975, were our No. 1 earner of foreign exchange. This strengthened the U.S. dollar and bought much-needed petroleum and mineral imports—and the consumer items so important to our level of living.

Cotton harvesters munch their way through a field, each picking as much in an hour as a man could pick in 72 hours. But it takes 100 acres of one-bale-to-the-acre cotton to make a mechanical picker pay. The hand pickers that have been replaced now work in industry and business producing other goods and services. U.S. agriculture is so efficient that only 4½ percent of the population is needed to produce our food and fiber. The key to our amazing affluence: the other 95½ percent produce other goods and services.

Opposite page
Tomatoes for processing can be picked mechanically because geneticists developed a firmer tomato that can take rough mechanical handling. After harvesters and 10-ton trailers have cleaned out this field in Yolo County, California, tomato plants are plowed under and another crop, perhaps sugar beets or barley, is planted. Double cropping is necessary to get the income to meet today's high costs of farming.

A farmers' co-op elevator waits to store the wheat being combined on a nearby farm at Farnam, Nebraska. Farmers own the elevator through the Farmers Cooperative Association, one of nearly 8,000 farmer supply and marketing cooperatives in the United States. Rather than being at the mercy of the price paid for wheat on the day of harvest, farmers can store in the elevator until they think the price is right. That's partly a guessing game, but farmers watch the news, keep an eye on the weather, and comb special publications for marketing intelligence. Since U.S. farmers must export two-thirds of their wheat, an event in Pakistan or in Rotterdam may affect a farmer's wheat prices more than what happens in the next county.

IF YOU
DON'T LIKE
FARMERS

THEN DON'T TALK
WITH YOUR
MOUTH FULL

PHOTOGRAPHED BY MARR

Every May the Lund Brothers of Minnesota truck their combines to Oklahoma and become part of a great custom harvest migration. Harvest crews follow the ripening grain northward to the Dakotas. The Lunds' machines combine some 50 acres a day apiece, with the Lunds charging about $8 an acre for the job. Custom operators need good weather, dependable machines, patience to do their own laundry, and huge quantities of fuel. An estimated 141 million gallons of petroleum fuel were needed by all farmers and operators to harvest the U.S. wheat crop in 1975. Finally, it is September and there is no more wheat to harvest in the Great Plains. Then the Lunds—Gordon, Irvin, Larry and Gary and their sons—head for Minnesota and a winter of school, odd jobs, mechanical repairs, trucking, flying and ice fishing.

Handling hay bales is a tough job, but Nancy Breneman, a secretary in an international program at the University of Minnesota, likes to keep her hand in helping her father, Clarence Lauck, on his farm near Canby, Minnesota. Most every farm girl or wife helps with the heavy work now and then when there's a rush job to finish. The farm wife is a full partner in managing and operating the family farm business.

Floyd and Davis Haas struggle to get the
last half-bale out of their baler. Many
farm tasks are two-man jobs, but that's
only one of the reasons why a high
percent of U.S. farms are partnerships,
mostly father-and-son and
brother-and-brother. Mainly, partnerships
are a way for a young man to meet the
staggering costs of getting started in
farming and to keep the farm in the family.

The whole corn plant, stalk and ears, is chewed up by this field chopper at Walworth, Wisconsin, and is blown into the trailing wagon. The succulent mixture of green stalks and grain is hauled to an upright silo or a horizontal trench silo for storing. Packed solid, it ferments slightly in its juices and remains a tasty dish for dairy cattle throughout the winter. What started as green leaves in a field converting energy from the sun's rays will end up as ice cream for dessert. That's what agriculture is all about.

Farmers continually check their equipment
for possible trouble. Paul Nelson, a district
conservationist who gets into wheat
harvesting while on vacation each year, is
checking the combine to see that all is
going well. Wheat is being cut on the Ralph
A. Hansen farm at Kingfisher, Oklahoma.

Both the alfalfa plants being windrowed in the foreground and the industrial plants silhouetted in the background have been making nitrogen fertilizer. Alfalfa, with the help of nitrogen-fixing microbes on its roots, converts nitrogen from the air into nutrients for the soil on the Jim Preece farm in the Imperial Valley in California. Beyond are the towers of Valley Nitrogen Producers, Inc., a farm-owned cooperative producing both liquid and dry fertilizers. Nitrogen is one of the modern miracles that helped raise U.S. corn yields from 42 bushels per acre in 1945 to 86 bushels per acre in 1975. It's one of the developments that keep food plentiful at reasonable prices.

That beautiful black oak that Jerry Cook
of Hartshorn, Missouri, is felling is a crop.
It just takes longer to mature than most
crops. It may end up as a beautiful piece
of furniture, or one of dozens of other
things. About 26 percent of the nation's
commercial timberland is on farms. To get
the wood we need when we want it takes
long-range planning. That may stretch
beyond a farmer's career; he needs to feel
that one day it will be a paying crop for
someone, perhaps his son.

More than 12 billion cubic feet of wood are harvested each year in the United States. People use it for houses and firewood, for letters and newspapers, to sit or ride on, to play upon, to wear and for a myriad of other uses. By the year 2000, American production of wood is expected to reach between 16.4 and 21.9 billion cubic feet—depending on prices. To meet this demand—and a lot of other needs such as a home for wildlife and recreation for city folks—there are 754 million acres of forest land in the United States. Two-thirds of that is capable of producing wood commercially, and more than 70 percent of it is privately owned.

There'll be a lot of good times around the fireplace when Brooks Mills' grey birch, harvested in Eddington, Maine, reaches its final destination. Helping Brooks in the invigorating work were Larry Petty, 16, and Brooks' son, John, 13. Brooks, who is driving the tracked vehicle especially adapted to logging, was a stockbroker but quit to raise organic produce, livestock, Christmas trees, pulpwood and firewood.

Apples such as these in Rappahannock
County, Virginia, provided a bumper
harvest of 7.2 billion pounds in 1975, at
least 7 percent higher than in any of the
previous 15 years. Most apples are sold in
the fresh market—kept fresh by controlled
atmospheric storage using carbon dioxide
gas. However, more and more people are
eating apples in some processed form.

OTIS

Mrs. Jose Lopez, a former Los Angeles
school teacher, is one of about 209,000
migrant workers in the United States
who make harvest time possible among
crops which are not harvested
mechanically. Nearly the entire apple
crop is picked by hand. Mrs. Lopez,
working in a Washington orchard, says
she is not a fast picker because she
is careful not to bruise the apples.

A bubble in a ripe cranberry makes this unique harvesting system possible in Massachusetts. Fields of cranberry bushes are flooded and a beater (opposite page) churns the berries off the bushes. The cranberries—with their bubbles—float to the surface. Harvesters using floating 2x4 or 2x6 "fences" or "booms" corral the cranberries into one corner of the harvested area for gathering and transporting to market. Workers (above) push the floating berries onto a conveyor belt, which lifts them into trucks. The cranberry harvest is valued at $24 million a year in the U.S.

A special machine slips a blade beneath the sod like a spatula under a pancake and rolls up sod in strips 18 inches wide and 6 feet long on the Tuckahoe Turf Farms, Slocum, Rhode Island. Another machine cuts strips 4 feet wide and 63 feet long for football fields and other large grass areas.

KARALES

The nursery business has its own form of harvesting. It's really transplanting—beautifying the face of urban America. New homes need new lawns, new shrubs, new trees and new flowers as soon as possible. Older lawns need a face lifting every now and then. The demand is insatiable and business is good. Sod alone is a quarter-billion dollar a year business.

Left
The nursery business has a hard time keeping up with demand. Sales spurted 30 percent between 1964 and 1969 and have grown tremendously since then. Trees and shrubs, such as those being moved at the Bald Hill Nurseries, Exeter, Rhode Island, help account for the $900 million annual wholesale nursery business in trees, shrubs and vines. There's also a big business in cut flowers, lettuce under glass, seeds, bulbs, and other items.

Too big to lift, so roll it. A lost fact:
who was the first to make a smiling
jack-o'-lantern? But hats off to the
jolly pumpkin in the Bicentennial year:
he's a native American all the way.

Harvesting cabbage is only partly
mechanized and is a job for a big crew
on the Krunmueller Farm near San Juan,
Texas. Workers cut the mature cabbage
heads and drop them onto a conveyor
belt which carries them to a wagon.
Immature heads may never be picked,
because it won't pay to go over the field
again. This hand-harvesting method has
been largely replaced by complete machine
harvesting. Cabbage ranks about 40th
among the 100 or so major crops harvested
by farmers.

Opposite page
Tobacco, one of America's earliest
commercial crops, is grown and cured in
many different ways for special uses. This
shade tobacco, grown under a cheesecloth
cover on the Phelps Kendrick Farm at
Windsor, Connecticut, is thin-leaved and
ideal for cigar wrapping. Teenager Bob
Phillips is carefully picking the leaves that
will bring about $6 a pound. Pickers make
about seven harvest runs during the
July-September season, taking only the
lower three leaves off each plant
during a run.

Pineapples are harvested once a year for three years—then yields drop sharply and the plants are plowed under. This was the second picking on the Richard Tayamahoshi farm, Hawaii. Pineapple production in the United States has dropped 26 percent in the last 10 years. Production has been shifting to the Philippines, Taiwan and Mexico, largely because of lower labor and land costs there. Yet 704,000 tons were produced in the U.S. in 1974.

Opposite page
Delicate handling is required for grapes headed for the fresh market. Laura Bowerman and grandson, Pat, help in the harvest. Nearly two-thirds of grapes produced in the U.S. go into wine, only 11 percent into the fresh market (the rest into raisins, juice and jelly). U.S. per capita wine consumption has increased 89 percent in the last 15 years.

Myron Nickerson lassoes barrels of potatoes on the ground and flicks a switch with his left hand to hoist them onto the flatbed truck. Steve Giberson rolls them into place. Workers fill the barrels by hand after the mechanical digger turns up the spuds near Presque Isle, Maine. Youngsters are still released from school to help during the Maine potato harvest; a practice once common in all rural America. The press of summer farm work is why we developed a tradition of winter school and summer vacations.

BOGRE

Production of sunflowers has skyrocketed
in recent years. In 1975, farmers harvested
1¼ million acres compared with only
53,000 acres ten years earlier. A special
head on the combine at Aberdeen, South
Dakota, harvests the seeds—which are
used mainly for cooking oils, salad oils,
margarine, mayonnaise, birdseed and
confections.

Catfish are harvested year-round and about 50 million pounds are produced each year in the U.S. Commercial production occupies about 55,000 acres of water. At the C. H. Block farm near Tunica, Mississippi, catfish are stocked at about 2,300 to the acre in 150 acres of pond area. Block was getting about 55 cents a pound for his fish in 1975.

Harvesting worms may not be everybody's idea of farming but Faye Hutchinson and her husband Harold make a living at it near Bolla, Missouri. Beds containing about 50,000 worms each are watered down each morning, then dusted with corn meal as a feed. About 200,000 of the older worms are picked and bagged each week, then delivered by Hutchinsons' crew to bait shops throughout Missouri and Arkansas.

PHOTOGRAPHED BY SCHUMAKER

One of the first signs of early spring in Vermont: sap buckets hanging on the maple trees. Farmers also collect sap with plastic pipes running from the trees to a tank or sugar house. Four generations of the Wright family of Enosburg, Vermont, use both the pipeline and the bucket method in their family syrup business. The sap is heated at the sugar house until it has the consistency of syrup. The early sap, gathered around mid-March in Vermont, provides the best grade of syrup (AA or Fancy), which Ruth Wright describes as having a "very light mellow soft maple flavor."

GEORGIA

That huge "marshmallow" of hay was
built to stay outdoors to provide feed for
livestock on the Darrell Wallace farm at
Britton, South Dakota. The hay is
windrowed, then blown onto a flatbed
trailer and compressed with huge winglike
metal arms. The system is not satisfactory
in damper climates because the hay
might spoil.

In dollars, hay is the fourth most valuable crop harvested
in the United States—more valuable than cotton and
tobacco combined. Yet harvesting can be the most
wretched work on a farm. First, the hay has to be the right
maturity, but loses its nutritive quality if it gets much
beyond that—and the weather has to be good. That means
hurry, hurry when things are just right. Hurrying often
involves hand-tossing bales that can weigh as much as 50
pounds each. Much of our nation's meat and milk supply
comes from grass and hay grown on rough land that
otherwise would be wasted.

One of the hottest jobs is catching bales of
hay at the end of an elevator and wrestling
them into place in the haymow. If the
haymow's under a tin roof on a humid day,
catching even a whiff of a breeze at the
open door is a lifesaver. The wide-spaced
boards in the Davis Haas barn help air
circulate to cure the hay. Wet hay
generates heat and spontaneous
combustion will burn down the barn.
The art is knowing when the hay is dry
enough to store, but not so dry the leaves
shatter off from handling.

Y ou help a neighbor in need; it's one of the things
you do. It has always been that way, from the time
pioneers helped a new neighbor raise a barn or build
a cabin. The fierce independence of farmers melts like
butter when a neighbor needs a hand. He'll pay it back
later, double fold, to you or someone else in need. Being
a good neighbor is the highest accolade in rural America.

When Frank Clayburg of Coon Rapids,
Iowa, was hospitalized, neighbors rolled in
with 10 corn combines and harvested his
100 acres in four hours.

Top right
Mrs. Lucille M. Lamp, co-owner of
the restaurant which provided free
meals to the Clayburg helpers,
serves the hungry men.

Joe Shirbroun stands on the combine
watching the last of Clayburg's grain
auger into the truck.

CONKLIN

When transportation problems arose at Yuton, Illinois, 800,000 bushels of corn from 1975's bumper crop had to be piled on the ground. The McLean County Service Company, which owns the elevators, eventually trucked the corn to Peoria, where barges moved it to downstream points. When transportation doesn't move the harvest, farmers' prices and incomes suffer. America's food supply, while bountiful, relies on an intricate transportation network moving it from farms, to processing plants, to your local store. Half the grain moving across international boundaries in 1975 was U.S. grain. To keep that market, we must be dependable suppliers—that includes getting it to the destination on time.

Tomorrow America will wake up hungry again. In the endless cycle of raising America's food, harvest is followed inevitably by preparation for another crop. This means plowing up the fields that raised this year's crops to get ready to plant next year, as Dave Kiley of St. Joseph, Iowa is doing. Whether this was a good year or a bad year for him, he must be an eternal optimist and expect next year to be better. The secret of our affluence is that he has an incentive to remain the world's most efficient supplier of food. In our system, the government doesn't tell him what to do; nor a foreman, a board nor a committee. He is what he is because his farm is his land, his home, and he is the planner, worker, manager, technician, and person who, along with his family, makes it go. The ingenuity and drive are his . . . as is his storehouse of knowledge, and the art and judgment born of experience, partly passed from generation to generation. It is all measured by his harvest. If his harvest, and that of 2.8 million other farmers, is good, then America eats well. If the incentive isn't there to work long hours, conserve the soil, take chances, endure the disappointments, go in debt, invest in machinery, keep up with modern methods—and if the income isn't there to make it possible—then we all fail with him.

ACKNOWLEDGEMENTS

PHOTOGRAPHERS

Gene Alexander; Lincoln, Nebraska
William Allard; Barboursville, Virginia
Gordon Baer; Cincinnati, Ohio
Linda Bartlett; Washington, D.C.
Robert Bjork; Washington, D.C.
Michelle Bogre; Columbia, Missouri
Don Breneman; St. Paul, Minnesota
David Brill; Cedar Grove, Wisconsin
Olivia Carlisle; Washington, D.C.
William Carnahan; Washington, D.C.
Jack Clark; Davis, California
Roy Clark; Columbus, Ohio
Paul Conklin; Washington, D.C.
Duane Dailey; Columbia, Missouri
Thomas DeFeo; Des Moines, Iowa
Nicholas deVore; Aspen, Colorado
Dana Downie; Riverside, California
Betsy Frampton; Washington, D.C.
Roland Freeman; Washington, D.C.
Paul Fusco; Mill Valley, California
George Gardner; Hillsdale, New York
Lowell Georgia; Arvada, Colorado
John Harvey; Wilmington, Delaware
Charles Herron; Washington, D.C.
B. Wolfgang Hoffman; Madison, Wisconsin
James Karales; New York, New York
Cornelius Keyes; Phoenix, Arizona
William Kuykendall; Hallsville, Missouri
Joseph Larson; Washington, D.C.
Michael Lawton; Falls Church, Virginia
Murray Lemmon; Washington, D.C.
Ray Lustig; Washington, D.C.
Bill Marr; Columbia, Missouri
Angus McDougall; Columbia, Missouri
Cal Olson; Fargo, North Dakota
Charles O'Rear; Arcadia, California
Lyle Orwig; Skokie, Illinois

Earl Otis; Puyallup, Washington
Marianne Pernold; Washington, D.C.
Suzanne Peterson; Sedona, Arizona
James Pickerell; Bethesda, Maryland
Larry Rana; Washington, D.C.
George Robinson; Washington, D.C.
John Running; Flagstaff, Arizona
Byron Schumaker; Washington, D.C.
Shepard Sherbell; Washington, D.C.
Bart Stewart; Lincoln, Nebraska
David Sutton; Washington, D.C.
David Warren; Washington, D.C.
John White; Denver, Colorado
Doug Wilson; Kirkland, Washington
Fred Witte; Washington, D.C.
Jonathan Wright; Aspen, Colorado

Front Cover photograph by DeFeo

The following State Cooperative Extension
Services provided photographic talent:
California . . . . Minnesota . . . .
Missouri . . . . Nebraska . . . .
Washington . . . . Wisconsin . . . .

STAFF

Concept
Claude Gifford

Development
David Granahan

Design
David Sutton
Kristina Jorgensen

Photography
Byron Schumaker
Joseph Larson
David Warren
Ovid Bay
Gary Nugent

Writing
John Harvey
John Crowley
Jack Hayes

Printing
Paul Wertz
Warren Bell

Support
Denver Browning
Stephen McKnight

This book was printed on an offset press. The
paper is 70 pound matte. Manuscript was set on
linotype in the type face Optima. Statements
are set 9/12 and captions 8/12, all regular. Chapter heads were set by a film phototypesetter in
48 point Oracle.

☆ U.S. Government Printing Office: 1976 0-200-300